THE SOCIETY OF THE SIGMA XI
DEVOTED TO THE
PROMOTION OF RESEARCH IN SCIENCE

National Lectureships

1941 and 1942

SCIENCE IN PROGRESS

THIRD SERIES

Science in Progress

By

HARLOW SHAPLEY	LIONEL S. MARKS
EDWIN HUBBLE	JAMES FRANCK
HANS A. BETHE	JOHN G. KIRKWOOD
V. K. ZWORYKIN	PERRIN H. LONG
P. W. BRIDGMAN	HERMANN MARK

Foreword by
WILLIS R. WHITNEY

Edited by
GEORGE A. BAITSELL

THIRD SERIES

New Haven
YALE UNIVERSITY PRESS

LONDON · HUMPHREY MILFORD · OXFORD UNIVERSITY PRESS

Preface

THE increasing recognition by those interested in science of the important and essentially unique function of *Science in Progress,* as a medium for the distribution of valuable research information from the various fields of science, has made possible the publication of this volume as the third in the series begun in 1939.

For those unfamiliar with these volumes, it may be well to state that the published material is based upon lectures presented in the National Sigma Xi Lectureships, given annually under Society auspices by a group of five distinguished scientists who are selected on the basis of outstanding contributions in their fields of research.

In the present volume, eight of the ten chapters are based on material presented in the 1941 and 1942 Lectureships. Chapter II of the present volume, by Dr. Edwin Hubble, was presented as the 20th Annual Sigma Xi Lecture at the meetings of the American Association for the Advancement of Science at Dallas, December, 1941. Chapter X was kindly released by Dr. Mark for publication at this time due to the current widespread interest in the problem of synthetic rubber, though the lecture will not be given for some months yet, in the 1943 Lectureships. Dr. I. Rabi of Columbia University and Dr. H. M. Evans of the University of California, lecturers in the 1941 and 1942 series respectively, were unable under present emergency conditions to prepare their lecture material for publication, but it is expected that their manuscripts will be included in the fourth volume of the series scheduled for publication in 1944.

The publication of this volume has been aided by funds received by the Sigma Xi Society from a legacy generously given by the late Professor E. J. Berg of Union College.

Some of the articles have appeared in the *American Scientist*, the Sigma Xi Quarterly.

The continued coöperation of the authors, the publisher, and the Society in the solution of the many problems inherent in the preparation and publication of these important contributions in permanent form is gratefully acknowledged by the editor.

GEORGE A. BAITSELL
National Secretary,
Society of the Sigma Xi

New Haven, Connecticut
October, 1942

Foreword

THERE is a peculiar persistence in scientific research, for which we should be thankful. Even when some intellectual leaders suggest a suspension of investigation lest we learn too much or too rapidly, the work of the scientist continues. "The gloomy dean," Inge of London, recently suggested a moratorium on science; and Herodotus much earlier put forth the same idea of the harmfulness of new knowledge—in this case, the working of iron and steel—upon advice received from the Oracle at Delphi. It is possible that the discoveries of the scientist at some time in the future may be used in totally good instead of partially evil ways, but meanwhile opinions differ. Our sense of devotion to truth gives us faith that ultimately something will be done about the goals of science and of scientists in what now seems to be an evil world. There appears to be no other honest way to proceed.

The discoveries of natural laws—laws which seem to have existed always—waited long for human appreciation. Yet the lure of discovery still encourages experimenters to proceed in the belief that there is no real limit to new knowledge and its service to mankind. In fact, the more each minute area of science is successfully explored by the inquisitive investigator, obviously the more extensive become the borderlands of human knowledge.

Relatively few individuals add to our store of knowledge, and to them the discovery of new truth appears as a sort of religion. It has always been so. The cave man, finding by experiment that flint made better tools than the materials previously used, exhibited a persistent hereditary character still evident in our aim at betterment. And we continue to be served by the important discoveries made long ages ago. For example, we still cook our food and make use of wheels for transportation. Later periods seem to have contributed to our advancement by new knowledge at nearly constant rates. Our appreciation, however, of the dim philosophies of past ages is not so clearly additive.

The important results of factual pioneering presented in this volume are new outgrowths of repeatable tests of natural laws—laws which antedate material creation—rather than philosophical speculations, which are often mystical fantasy. All that we observe of the processes of creation, including the acquisition of new knowledge, depends upon these eternal and unalterable laws of nature which man is privileged to discover and to appreciate.

WILLIS R. WHITNEY

Schenectady, N. Y.
August, 1942

Contents

Illustrations

Science in Progress

Science in Progress

I

GALAXIES

By HARLOW SHAPLEY

Harvard University

LIKE the galaxies themselves, the field of inquiry concerning galaxies is large and not easily surveyed in a brief article. It will be well to restrict the assignment and write only concerning a few selected topics.

Let us first try a bird's-eye view of our own Galaxy. The bird whose eye we would use needs to be a remarkable creature to reach the remoteness necessary for an outside look. We cannot use Cygnus, the Swan, that heads in full flight along the northern Milky Way, nor Aquila, the Eagle, nor the big-billed Toucan, the Flamingo, the Phoenix, the Goose, the Bird of Paradise, nor Corvus, the Crow. All these constellation birds are composed of stars that are bright neighbors of the Sun and distinctly localized far inside our own Galaxy.

What we need is an observation point something like a million light-years distant, well outside the bounds of the enormous Milky Way system. It would be pretty satisfactory to settle our bird comfortably in the outer haze of stars of the Andromeda Nebula. If the observer be a contemporary of ours, he will be looking at our system in terms of 8,000 centuries ago. It has been that long since the radiation left the Sun and its neighboring stars on its way to the retina of the all-comprehending but quite imaginary bird now surveying us from the Andromeda galaxy.

Such a temporal disparity, 8×10^5 years, is of no particular moment in our considerations of the galaxies; and short-term enterprises like the current Western civilization, or even the whole history of mankind, can be neglected in the cosmic panorama as too momentary, too fleeting, for a clear recording.

Fig. 1. The southern spiral, Messier 83.

It is well known that the Milky Way star system is a much flattened organization and that the Sun and planets are well inside. This interpretation of the Milky Way was pointed out 190 years ago by Thomas Wright, a pioneer "bird's-eye viewer" of Durham, England. He saw that the hypothesis of a flattened stellar system with the Earth near the central plane would satisfactorily explain the Milky

Way band as a phenomenon of projection in such a system.* Our hypothetical observer in Andromeda would see this flattened wheel-shaped system not from the direction of its rim, nor from the direction of its axis, but from an intermediate position, galactic latitude —21°. It would appear in projection, therefore, as an elongated object, perhaps with the axes of the rough ellipse in the ratio of about 3 to 1. There would be a conspicuous globular nucleus of naked-eye brightness.

We are almost certain now that our Galaxy is a great open-work spiral system of stars, perhaps not much unlike the system Messier 83, shown in Figure 1. But in linear measure it may be much larger than Messier 83. It has taken a long time to get conclusive evidence on the structure of our own system. We are badly located. There are obvious difficulties with residing inside. The meadow violet, no matter how bold and sensitive, is at a disadvantage in meadow topography compared with the bird hovering above.

For more than a hundred years astronomers have struggled with the problems of the structure of the Galaxy. There have been many speculators, but also some hard and systematic observers. Sir William Herschel dominated this field throughout the early part of the nineteenth century. His surveys of star clusters and nebulae, his measures of brightness and position of various celestial objects, his interpretations of the accumulating materials were so important that he is appropriately considered the founder of sidereal astronomy. Before him the emphasis was on comets and planets and the positions and motions of near-by stars and the laws governing these motions. It was essentially solar-system astronomy that attracted the telescopes and the wisdom of scientists until this German-Anglican organist of

---

* For an account of the early cosmic interpretations by Thomas Wright and Immanuel Kant see the highly interesting account by F. A. Paneth, *The Observatory* (June, 1941), pp. 71 ff.; also H. Shapley, chap. v, *Immanuel Kant, 1724-1924* (New Haven, Yale University Press, 1925), E. C. Wilm, ed.

Bath devised some instruments; then astronomy turned outward to interstellar spaces.

Sir William Herschel was considerably baffled by the problem of the structure of the Galaxy and by the relation of clusters and nebulae to the Milky Way. His successors made many notable contributions, photometric and spectroscopic, to knowledge of the nature of stars and nebulae, but still the large cosmic problems remained baffling. Increasing telescopic strength, however, and the accumulation of many kinds and types of observations, eventually led to less puzzlement about the stellar neighbors of the Sun and the nearer parts of the Milky Way. The old but unproved concept that the spiral nebulae and their relatives were external galaxies, coördinate with our own Milky Way system, gradually became established. The dimensions of the Galaxy and of the universe approached clarification, chiefly through the power of the telescopes of American observatories and the vision of European and American theoreticians.

In clarifying some of the earlier puzzles, however, the astronomers only succeeded in opening vaster vistas for exploration, interpretation, and wonderment. The net gain has been considerable. It is no longer believed that the difficulties of certain astronomical enterprises have definitely blocked the progress of inquiry. A hundred years ago a distinguished scientist (not an astronomer) gloated a bit over the pronouncement that one thing would certainly forever remain unknown, namely, the chemical nature of the stars! It was not many years before the spectroscope began to betray him. Up to the time of her death Dr. Annie Cannon had classified more than half a million stars in detail on the basis of the chemistry of their surfaces. A great deal is now known of the chemical constitution of a galaxy of a billion stars at a distance of 10 million light-years. An elementary astronomical student can quickly learn, with the use of modern equipment, about the hydrogen, calcium, iron, magnesium, helium, carbon, and the like in stars that have never actually been seen except by use of the photographic plate.

FIG. 2. The southern globular star cluster, 47 Tucanae.

The moral of that bad ancient pronouncement about stellar chemistry is that it is not wise to be discouraged with the difficulties arising from our awkward location in the Galaxy. Eventually all the answers to all the questions you could now ask about Millky Way structure may be known. And, of course, then we would be wise enough to ask other questions that you could not answer, nor could we. Here are some of the current questions, and, for some of them, preliminary answers.

1. Are the Sun and its planets in the middle of our discoidal Galaxy? They certainly are not. There are many lines of evidence which indicate that the center is far away in the direction of the region where the constellations of Sagittarius, Ophiuchus, and Scorpio come together, 30° or a little more south of the celestial equator in the thick of the bright star clouds along the Milky Way. My early study of the globular star clusters (a reproduction of an important one, 47 Tucanae, is shown in Figure 2) was instrumental in showing the observer that he is well out toward the rim of the wheel-shaped Galaxy. There may be some "subcenters" in other parts of the Milky Way, in far south Carina, for instance, and in Cygnus. But those conglomerations of stars appear to be important local structures within the great Galaxy that has its massive nucleus in the Sagittarius direction.

2. Is this Galaxy in motion as a unit? How it moves with respect to near-by galaxies is not yet very clear, but certainly it rotates around the Sagittarius nucleus. It does not rotate as a solid wheel, at least at our distance from the nucleus. It rotates more as the planetary system rotates; the planets nearer the Sun go more rapidly and complete their "years" in shorter times than the remoter planets. We think we can very definitely measure the differential speed of stars around the nucleus. The average speed in the Sun's neighborhood is about 200 miles a second, and the direction of motion is toward the northern constellation of Cygnus.

3. How far are the Sun and the neighboring stars from the axis of rotation? Ten kiloparsecs is the approximate answer and, since a parsec is 3.26 light-years or about 20 trillion miles, the distance is something like 2×10^{17} miles, or 30-odd thousand light-years. For various reasons, that value of 10 kiloparsecs is not too certain, but it is well estab-

lished that the center of gravity of our system is between 8 and 12 kiloparsecs distant. The direction to the center is fixed with an uncertainty of only 2° or 3°; this angular parameter is much easier to handle than the distance.

FIG. 3. The nucleus of our own galactic system. Among the millions of distant stars, whose light builds up the central star clouds, are thousands of variable stars.

4. How large is the Milky Way system and how populous? Enormous in size and population, if nonquantitative terms may be used. There is good evidence that the total population in stars is of the order of 200,000 million, but the evidence on over-all dimensions is as yet inconclusive.

Indeed it is somewhat involved with definitions. For instance, what constitutes the boundary of a galaxy? Is it at the distance of the furthermost discoverable member of the system? Or is it the distance to the place where the number of stars per cubic light-year has decreased to a specified small quantity? Or is it, for a spiral galaxy, the distance to which a spiral arm can be traced? Or is it the distance to which an escaping star can go before the gravitational hold-back is exceeded by the pull from some other galaxy?

The diameter of the system in its plane is not less than 100,000 light-years if all its recognizable stars are included. There is now good evidence that the wheel-shaped system is surrounded by a more or less spherical haze of stars, and some of the stars in the haze are 50,000 light-years above the plane of the Milky Way. Probably this haze extends more distantly in the plane of the system and, therefore, the diameter of discoid plus haze considerably exceeds 100,000 light-years.

On the other hand, the diameter of our system in its plane might be measured as only 50,000 light-years, or even less, if we had to depend on photographic research equipment which, although comparable with our own, was located in the Virgo supergalaxy, several million light-years away. Our outer stars might not register. When our telescopes are turned on the members of that group in Virgo we can trace on the best of our long-exposure plates the largest individual galaxies only to a distance of 10,000 or 15,000 light-years from their centers. Either those systems are very much smaller than ours, or we are unable to explore the faint regions that are as remote from the nuclei as we are from our nucleus in Sagittarius.

It might turn out, therefore, that the bird's-eye observer from the Andromeda Nebula would report that our galactic system is no larger than the Andromeda Nebula; or, if the research were rather casual, the view might include only the nuclear portions of our galactic system, which might even be catalogued as a spheroidal galaxy. When we, in our turn, take a quick bird's-eye view of the Andromeda galaxy,

Fig. 4. Light and darkness surrounding Eta Carinae, which was a nova a century ago and now is a peculiar eighth-magnitude variable star. The photograph was made with the Rockefeller Reflector on Harvard Kopje near Bloemfontein, South Africa.

and measure its distance and dimensions, we immediately conclude that it is much smaller than we are, even though it is a giant compared with the average galaxy of our catalogues. But when the over-all extent of the Andromeda galaxy is studied with precise measuring apparatus, we

double the dimensions as first seen and conclude that it is
not very much smaller than the Milky Way system.

FIG. 5. Star clouds and nebulosity of suggestive outline in the northern Milky Way.
Photograph made at the Hamburg Observatory with a Schmidt-type reflector.

5. Why is it that we seem to be so baffled about the structure and dimensions of our own system, although we
bravely go out to distances of 100 million light-years in our
explorations of other galaxies? What is so troublesome

about measuring something that completely surrounds us and is near at hand?

That question finally brings out one feature of Milky Way structure which must be clearly seen at first glance by the observer in Andromeda, but which has taken us many years and much labor to discover and partially evaluate. This basic feature (and difficulty) is the presence throughout the Milky Way, especially near the Milky Way plane, of interstellar absorbing material—dust and gas, scattered and in clouds, around the stars and in the spaces between them. Our vision is not clear; simple geometric relations between light and distance are incorrect because our observing station is in a fog that unevenly dims the light of the surrounding stars.

Gradually we are learning through studies of colors, and otherwise, how to make corrections for the interstellar absorption. It would not be difficult at all if the absorbing material were uniform. But the clouds of absorption are irregular. It is supposed that some of the greatest irregularities would be apparent to the Andromedan observer. At any rate, our own bird's-eye views of hundreds of external galaxies show immediately the dark lanes between spiral arms, or across them, which indicate the interstellar absorption clouds that irregularly dim the star fields of those distant stellar systems.

In summary, our imaginary bird's-eye view has revealed our system as discoidal in its main body of stars, probably surrounded by a thinly populated spheroidal shell and dominated by a massive globular nucleus, which is some 30,000 light-years from the Sun in an accurately measurable direction. Less certainly the view discloses that the Milky Way system is a spiral, perhaps more open in structure than the Andromeda galaxy; it is rotating at high speed, but even so two million centuries to complete one circuit, to click off one cosmic year. Uncertainty remains as to over-all dimensions of the discoidal Galaxy and of its stellar haze, and this uncertainty arises in part from the light-absorbing, mostly nonluminous, interstellar material

FIG. 6. The axis and outlying star clusters of the Large Magellanic Cloud—the nearest of external galaxies. Photograph made in Peru at the Boyden Station of the Harvard Observatory with the 8-inch Bache telescope. This nearest of external galaxies is about 75,000 light-years distant.

and from its irregular distribution and its dissimilar effectiveness on light at various wave lengths.

If for a more distant view of this part of the universe we go off into space several million light-years in a special direction, the Andromeda Nebula and our galactic system would look like a pair of galaxies, separated by only a few diameters. And in the same field, apparently also a part of our local group of galaxies, would be the great spiral, Messier 33. A closer inspection from this distant point, and a careful measurement of distances, would show several

FIG. 7. NGC 55, an external galaxy without visible nucleus. This object may be less than 2 million light-years distant; it may be one of our neighbors. Photographed with the Rockefeller Reflector.

fainter galaxies associated with these three large systems. Two of them would be the faint companions of the Andromeda Nebula—Messier 32 and NGC 205; two of them would be our own satellite-companions, the Large and Small Clouds of Magellan. And there would be at least four other dwarf galaxies, two of them irregular in form, and two or more spheroidal.

The existence of this local cloud of galaxies, in which our

system appears to be the big dominating member, seems
to be now beyond question, but the census of its membership is not complete. All the known members are within a

Fig. 8. The ring-tail nebula in Corvus—in form one of the most remarkable of
external galaxies.

sphere of a million light-years' diameter. Those unknown,
or of uncertain membership, include systems wholly or
partly concealed by the clouds of absorption near the Milky
Way plane. The rating of the great globular clusters is also
not yet clear. A hundred globular clusters surround our

galaxy, apparently subordinate members of the system, but the larger ones, like Omega Centauri and 47 Tucanae, should perhaps be ranked with the dwarf galaxies. In total luminosity and in mass they are comparable to NGC 205, the faint spheroidal galaxy in the Andromeda group. Our hypothetical Andromedan observer would probably record at least these two giant clusters as dwarf galaxies, if our own procedure with regard to classifying NGC 205 was followed.

Groups like the local "supergalaxy" occur elsewhere in metagalactic space. A dozen rich clusters are known, some of them with hundreds of members, and a score or two of small groups, similar to our own, are already on record. One such is a group of objects in Fornax, in which the brightest are spheroidal; in our group the brightest galaxies are spiral or irregular in form.

Probably there are dwarf galaxies in the Fornax group, but as yet we have not identified them, nor have we found the Magellanic type. Because of the general tendency of the universe to expand and the galaxies and groups of galaxies to recede from one another, it may be that eventually we shall be able to say which faint objects in Fornax are members of the supersystem simply by determining their velocities in the line of sight. If the suspected galaxy is really much more distant than the average of the Fornax group, it will show a bigger "red shift" in the spectrum, a greater velocity of recession, and thus intimate the larger distance and nonmembership.

On every expedition into remote corners of extragalactic space, it is necessary to equip ourselves with information on giant and supergiant stars. The reason is, obviously, that ordinary stars in far-off places are not recorded on our photographs; they are too dim. We must work with the giants. It may be of interest to consider the following highly luminous stars and types of stars and see how they contribute to knowledge of the metagalaxy:

1. Supernovae; 2. S Doradus; 3. Novae; 4. P-Cygni Stars and Others.

1. "The most energetic catastrophe in the history of the world, unless it be creation itself," is how I would describe the great violence of radiation and motion that accompanies the career of the supernova. Simply defined, a supernova results when a star blows up. Whether the disaster is caused or encouraged by head-on collision with another star or another something, or by the collapse of the star's structure, with the consequent atomic transformation of mass into radiation, or "just happens," we cannot yet say. More observational data are needed and are being obtained. The result of a supernova outburst is the outpouring of light in unparalleled fashion—a spurt of radiation the equivalent at times of 50 million suns and more. The burst of radiation lasts sometimes several days or weeks, quieting down slowly as the months go by. What remains after the flare-up? Perhaps a dense subdwarf star (the collapsed core of the original star) ; perhaps a hurriedly expanding nebula; perhaps just dust and ashes, and the Universe filling up with the dying glow of a radiant moment.

Dr. Fritz Zwicky of the California Institute of Technology has been the leader in recent years in the discovery of supernovae and in speculations concerning them. He thinks that neutrons and neutrinos play an important part in the supernova phenomenon. Certainly supernovae play a significant part in the history of the Universe. They are not too uncommon. About 40 are on record, most of them discovered in the past 10 years. Three of them appeared in our own galactic system. One hypothesis of the origin of the cosmic rays ties them up with the violence of the supernova.

The most distant individual stars yet photographed are some of the supernovae that are in galaxies tens of millions of light-years distant. When more complete records are secured we shall be able to see if, at maximum brightness, they are sufficiently alike so that their apparent magnitudes at maximum can be used as a practical criterion of distance. At present there seems to be too large a dispersion in the intrinsic luminosities to make supernovae useful criteria in distance measurement in the metagalaxy.

Long before supernovae were recognized, and long before there was the faintest notion of their enormous size as celestial phenomena, they played a very important part in astronomical development and knowledge of the Universe. For it happens that new stars suddenly appearing in 1572 and 1604 were important in the inspiration of two of the great astronomers of that time and of all time—Tycho Brahe, the Dane, and Johannes Kepler. Now we know that these stellar outbursts in Cassiopeia (Tycho's star) and in Ophiuchus (Kepler's *stella nova*) were most probably supernovae. Both stars rose to a brightness comparable with that of the brightest planet; both stars changed explosively 15 magnitudes or more, an increase of brightness of more than a million times.

A third supernova of our galactic system was recorded by the Japanese and Chinese astronomers in 1054. The phenomenon was the parent of the present well-known Crab Nebula which is still rapidly expanding as a result of the eleventh-century disaster—eleventh century in our records, but 5,000 years earlier on the cosmic clock.

2. *The Supergiant S Doradus.* The distinction of holding top place as a luminous star has been the lot of an object at the edge of one of the open clusters in the Large Magellanic Cloud. It is a variable star with average luminosity half a million times that of the Sun. It is somewhat exceeded in radiation output by supernovae, but they do not last, whereas S Doradus has been continuously radiating for the past half century, pouring out more than 100 trillion tons

of light per minute. It must have enormous resources to persist at such high luminosity. Is it perhaps some very slow type of supernova? The variations we now observe are irregular in character, but of no great moment in alleviating the expenditure of radiant energy. The spectrum of the star is of the rare P-Cygni type, which is indicative of unusually hot surface conditions. The Harvard photographic records of this star do not extend much before 1890, but of course there is little reason to suspect that S Doradus has been the supreme supergiant for only the past brief 50 years. Recent photographs with the large southern reflector have shown that stars nearly as bright as S Doradus are clustered around it, but unfortunately all of them are difficult to study because, notwithstanding their great intrinsic luminosities, the intervening distance of 75,000 light-years dims the light so that even large telescopes can with difficulty make detailed analyses. None of the stars in the solar neighborhood is one tenth as bright as S Doradus. In August 1942 Dr. S. Gaposchkin presented evidence from Harvard plates that S Doradus may be an eclipsing binary with a period of 40 years, thus adding to the wonder and mystery of this supergiant.

3. *Ordinary Novae*. Several times a year, if we pay close attention, we find new stars in our own galactic system, especially in the direction toward the galactic center in Sagittarius. But daylight, clouds, moonlight, and astronomical inactivity contribute to our failure to record more than a few per cent of those that we know, from sampling, must be occurring. These new stars, or ordinary novae, behave much like the supernovae described above. But the phenomenon is much less violent, and a star is not sacrificed by each outburst. It is likely that the ordinary nova represents the explosive instability of the outer surfaces of a star. There is some indication that before explosion the ordinary novae are slightly subnormal stars of ordinary type. Per-

haps this subnormality is at the bottom of the trigger action that sets them off.

But whatever the cause of the novae, it must be recorded as an interesting phenomenon, and one that probably is important in the general history of stars. In our own Galaxy, and in the neighboring Andromeda galaxy, these novae appear so frequently that when one thinks back over the past billion years that the Earth's crust has existed, one concludes that very many stars have shot the works—a large proportion of them. Frequently we have remarked that novation is so common and time has been so long that every star might have blown up once, or will blow up during the next billions years—in other words, that evolution, or development, by way of the nova outburst is a major and not a negligible phenomenon in this world.

Evidence is accruing, however, that novation is a recurrent phenomenon. Four or five stars have been novae more than once, and two of them three times since 1860. If this be the true situation—only stars of peculiar character becoming novae—we may remain even more at ease with respect to the immediate future of our Sun. Its character is good and normal. We like to believe that the Sun is and always will be only slightly variable (in the sun-spot period), and will remain quite dependable, undisturbed by interstellar clouds, unsusceptible to nova-inciting disturbance—at least for the next thousand years while the astronomers are finding out about the Universe. A nova-like change in the Sun would promptly wipe biology off the Earth, if it did not erase the planet altogether.

At maximum the ordinary novae are supergiant stars, more than 10,000 times the luminosity of the Sun, but scarcely 1 per cent as radiant as the average supernova. When novae appear in external galaxies they can be used as distance indicators because at maximum brightness the ordinary nova comes to about the same candle power every time. Comparing the apparent brightness with the real brightness, the distance in light-years can readily be computed. Next to the Cepheid variables, novae are the best criteria for measuring distances of galaxies, providing there are enough found in any given system to stabilize the statistics.

4. *Some Other Supergiants.* Two or three magnitudes fainter than the notable S Doradus in the Large Magellanic Cloud are a number of others of the same peculiar spectrum, which are termed the P-Cygni type. There is evidence, not quite conclusive, that these stars are related to the novae, differing most conspicuously, of course, in the property of remaining at high luminosities and not fading away after the impulsive outburst. But in addition to these bluish hot stars we find in the Magellanic Clouds supergiant red stars, almost as bright. Some of them are variable, and some are, indeed, long-period Cepheid variables, 10,000 times as bright as the Sun. Many resemble the famous red giants of our neighborhood, Antares and Betelgeuse. A few greatly exceed the local red supergiants in volume as well as in radiation output. Diameters of the order of the radius of Jupiter's orbit, volumes ten million times that of the Sun, are indicated. These preposterous dimensions are derived by knowing the distance of the Magellanic Cloud, the total candle powers of these supergiant stars, and the spectra which indicate low efficiency as radiators. In order to give out so much radiation, the emitting surfaces must be exceedingly large. The star S Doradus, on the other hand, which is a more efficient radiator, is much smaller and denser than the Antares-like supergiants.

Adjacent to the Small Magellanic Cloud is the great globular cluster, 47 Tucanae, already mentioned as an intermediate between normal galaxies and normal star clusters. Its three brightest stars appear to be typical long-period variable stars, but they are not typical in one respect.

Their luminosities at maximum are 3 or 4 magnitudes brighter than most long-period variable stars, which are typified by Mira (The Wonderful) Ceti, the first of known variables. It is peculiar, too, that the 3 supergiant variables in the cluster rise to almost exactly the same magnitude at maximum, and all have periods of about 200 days. This is one of the coincidences that the laws of chance do not easily condone; there must be some deep significance for stars or star clusters in the unusual performance of these supergiants.

Both blue and red supergiants appear sporadically in our own galactic system; probably the occasionally detectable highly luminous stars in external galaxies also belong to various spectral classes. Hubble has effectively used the luminosities of these invariable stars, along with the available information on Cepheid variables and ordinary novae, to get the distances of galaxies that are not more than a few million light-years away. If a galaxy is as much as 20 million light-years distant, even these supergiants cannot be individually photographed with present telescopic and photographic equipment, and resort must be made to other photometric means of estimating distances. Ordinary giant stars, like Vega and Arcturus, are not yet photographed in any but the very nearest galaxies, and stars of average mass and luminosity, like the Sun, have so far not been photographed outside our own galactic system.

The future of research on galaxies probably depends not so much on the size of telescopes as on the speed and resolution of photographic plates and on other radiation-registering devices. But even without better facilities than those at present available, astronomers have plenty to do in galactic research, for within reach are 1,000 million individual stars in our own Galaxy, and at least 10 million other galaxies.

For References see p. 297.

THE PROBLEM OF THE EXPANDING UNIVERSE

By EDWIN HUBBLE

Mt. Wilson Observatory

I PROPOSE to discuss the problem of the expanding universe from the observational point of view. The fact that such a venture is permissible is emphatic evidence that empirical research has definitely entered the field of cosmology. The exploration of space has swept outward in successive waves, first through the system of the planets, then through the stellar system, and finally into the realm of the nebulae. Today we study a region of space so vast and so homogeneous that it may well be a fair sample of the universe. At any rate, we are justified in adopting the assumption as a working hypothesis and attempting to infer the nature of the universe from the observed characteristics of the sample. One phase of this ambitious project is the observational test of the current theory of the expanding universes of general relativity.

I shall briefly describe the observable region of space as revealed by preliminary reconnaissance with large telescopes, then sketch the theory in outline, and finally discuss the recent more accurate observations that were designed to clarify and to test the theory.

THE OBSERVABLE REGION

The sun, as you know, is a star, one of several thousand million stars which together form the stellar system. This system is a great swarm of stars isolated in space. It drifts through the universe as a swarm of bees moves through the

summer air. From our position near the sun we look out
through the swarm of stars, past the borders, and into the
universe beyond.

Fig. 9. Messier 31. The outer regions of the great spiral in Andromeda, when photographed with the 100–inch reflector, are partially resolved into stars. Among these
stars several types are recognized which are well known in our own stellar system.
Since we know their intrinsic luminosity (candle power), their apparent faintness
indicates the distance of the nebula—about 700,000 light-years.

Distances have been determined in this manner for a sample collection of neighboring nebulae. The results serve to calibrate various other criteria of distances which
are less precise but can be applied out as far as nebulae can be observed.

Until recently those outer regions lay in the realm of
speculation. Today we explore them with confidence. They
are empty for the most part, vast stretches of empty space.
But here and there, separated by immense intervals, other
stellar systems are found, comparable with our own. We
find them thinly scattered through space out as far as tele-

scopes can reach. They are so distant that, in general, they appear as small faint clouds mingled among the stars, and many of them have long been known by the name "nebulae." Their identification as great stellar systems, the true inhabitants of the universe, was a recent achievement of great telescopes.

On photographs made with such instruments, these nebulae, these stellar systems, appear in many forms. Nevertheless they fall naturally into an ordered sequence ranging from compact globular masses through flattening ellipsoids into a line of unwinding spirals. The array exhibits the progressive development of a single basic pattern, and is known as the sequence of classification. It may represent the life history of stellar systems. At any rate, it emphasizes the common features of bodies that belong to a single family.

Consistent with this interpretation is the fact that these stellar systems, regardless of their structural forms, are all of the same general order of intrinsic luminosity; that is, of candle power. They average about 100 million suns and most of them fall within the narrow range from one-half to twice this average value. Giants and dwarfs are known, 10 to 20 times brighter or fainter than the average, but their numbers appear to be relatively small. This conclusion is definitely established in the case of giants, which can be readily observed throughout an immense volume of space, but is still speculative in the case of dwarfs which can be studied only in our immediate vicinity.

The limited range in luminosity is important because it offers a convenient measure of distance. As a first approximation, we may assume that the nebulae are all equally luminous, and, consequently, that their apparent faintness indicates their distances. The procedure is not reliable in the case of a single object because the particular nebula might happen to be a giant or a dwarf rather than a normal stellar system. But for statistical purposes, where large

numbers of nebulae are involved, the relatively few giants
and dwarfs should average out, and the mean distances of
large groups may be accurately determined. It is by this

FIG. 10. A group of nebulae. The four nebulae NGC 3185, 3187, 3190, and 3193
form a quadruple system in which various types of structural forms are well represented. The distance is about 8 million light-years. Each nebula is a stellar system,
the intrinsic luminosities ranging from 60 to 170 million suns.

method that the more remote regions of space, near the
limits of the telescope, may be explored with confidence.

Throughout the observable region the nebulae are found
scattered singly, in pairs, and in groups up to great compact clusters or even clouds. The small-scale distribution

is irregular, and is dominated by a tendency toward cluster-
ing. Yet when larger and larger volumes of space are compared, the minor irregularities tend to average out, and the

Fig. 11. A cluster of nebulae. The Corona Borealis cluster is a compact globular
cluster of several hundred nebulae at a distance of about 130 million light-years. The
photograph made with the 100-inch reflector, shows the central region in which the
nebulae are more numerous than the foreground stars. The brightest nebulae in
clusters offer favorable opportunties to study objects at vast distances.

samples grow more and more uniform. If the observable
region were divided into a hundred or even a thousand
equal parts, the contents would probably be nearly identical. Therefore, the large-scale distribution of nebulae is said

to be uniform; the observable region is homogeneous, very much the same everywhere and in all directions.

We may now present a rough sketch of our sample of the universe. The faintest nebulae that can be detected with the largest telescope in operation (the 100-inch reflector on Mount Wilson) are about 2 million times fainter than the faintest star that can be seen with the naked eye. Since we know the average candle power of these nebulae, we can estimate their average distance—500 million light-years. A sphere with this radius defines the observable region of space. Throughout the sphere are scattered about 100 million nebulae, at various stages of their evolutional development. These nebulae average about 100 million times brighter than the sun and several thousand million times more massive. Our own stellar system is a giant nebula, and is presumably a well-developed, open spiral. The nebulae are found, as has been said, singly, in groups and in clusters but, on the grand scale, these local irregularities average out and the observable region as a whole is approximately homogeneous. The average interval between neighboring nebulae is about 2 million light-years, and the internebular space is sensibly transparent.

THE LAW OF RED SHIFTS

Another general characteristic of the observable region has been found in the law of red shifts, sometimes called the velocity-distance relation. This feature introduces the subject of spectrum analysis. It is well known that, in general, light from any source is a composite of many individual colors or wave lengths. When the composite beam passes through a glass prism or other suitable device, the individual colors are separated out in an ordered rainbow sequence, known as a spectrum. The prism bends the light waves according to the wave length. The deflections are least for the long waves of the red and are greatest for the short waves of the violet. Hence position in the spectrum indicates the wave length of the light falling at any particular place in the sequence.

Incandescent solids, and certain other sources, radiate light of all possible wave lengths, and their spectra are continuous. Incandescent gases, however, radiate only certain particular wave lengths, and their spectra, called emission spectra, consist of various isolated colors separated by blank spaces. The patterns are well known, hence gases in a distant light source can be identified by their spectra.

The sun presents a third kind of spectrum, known as an absorption spectrum. The main body of the sun furnishes a continuous spectrum. The heavy atmosphere surrounding the main body is gaseous and would normally exhibit an emission spectrum. Actually, the atmosphere, because it is cooler than the main body, absorbs from the continuous background those colors it would otherwise emit. Therefore the solar spectrum is a continuous spectrum on which is superposed a pattern of dark gaps or lines. These dark lines identify the gases in the solar atmosphere and indicate the physical conditions under which they exist.

The nebulae are stellar systems, and their spectra resemble that of the sun. Dark lines due to calcium, hydrogen, iron, and other elements in the atmospheres of the component stars are identified with complete confidence. In the case of the nearer nebulae, these lines are close to their normal positions as determined in the laboratory or in the sun. In general, however, accurate measures disclose slight displacements, either to the red or to the violet side of the exact normal positions.

Such small displacements are familiar features in the spectra of stars and are known to be introduced by rapid motion in the line of sight. If a star is rapidly approaching the observer, the light waves are crowded together and shortened, and all the spectral lines appear slightly to the

violet side of the normal positions. Conversely, rapid recession of a star drags out and lengthens the light waves, and

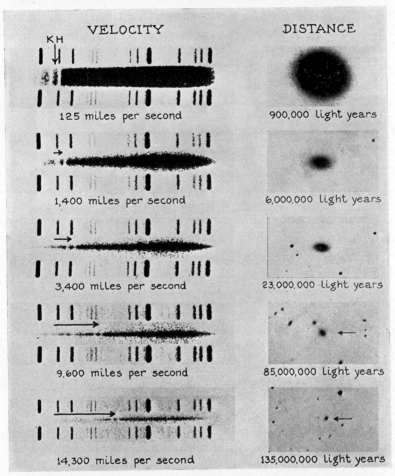

VELOCITY   DISTANCE

K H

125 miles per second   900,000 light years

1,400 miles per second   6,000,000 light years

3,400 miles per second   23,000,000 light years

9,600 miles per second   85,000,000 light years

14,300 miles per second   135,000,000 light years

FIG. 12. The velocity-distance relation for extra-galactic nebulae.

the spectral lines are seen to the red of their normal positions.

The amounts of these displacements (they are called

Doppler shifts) indicate the velocities of the stars in the line of sight. If the wave lengths are altered by a certain fraction of the normal wave lengths, the star is moving at a velocity which is that same fraction of the velocity of light. In this way it has been found that the stars are drifting about at

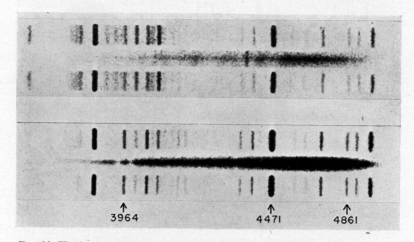

FIG. 13. The largest red shift. The upper spectrum (brightest nebula in the Bootes cluster, distance about 240 million light-years) shows the largest well-determined red shift hitherto recorded. The H and K lines are found near the strong helium line, 4,471 Å, in the comparison spectrum, while their normal positions (shown in the lower spectrum, NGC 3898) are near the comparison line 3,964. The shift of 516 Å corresponds with a velocity of recession of 24,500 miles per second.

The emission line in the upper spectrum, to the left of H and K, is the mercury line, 4,358, introduced by the reflection in the sky of the lights in Los Angeles and its suburbs. Both spectra were obtained by Humason using the 100-inch reflector.

average speeds of 10 to 30 miles per second, and, indeed, that the stellar system, our own nebula, is rotating about its center at the majestic rate of one revolution in perhaps 200 million years.

Similarly, the nebulae are found to be drifting about in space at average speeds of the order of 150 miles per second. Such speeds, of course, are minute fractions of the velocity of light, and the corresponding Doppler shifts, which may be either to the violet or to the red, are barely perceptible.

But the spectra of distant nebulae show another effect as conspicuous as it is remarkable. The dark absorption lines are found far to the red of their normal positions. Superposed on the small red or violet shifts representing individual motions, is a systematic shift to the red which increases directly with the distances of the nebulae observed. If one nebula is twice as far away as another, the red shift will be twice as large; if *n* times as far away, the red shift will be *n* times as large. This relation is known as the law of red shifts; it appears to be a quite general feature of the observable region of space.

If these systematic red shifts are interpreted as the familiar Doppler shifts, it follows that the nebulae are receding from us in all directions at velocities that increase directly with the momentary distances. The rate of increase is about 100 miles per second per million light-years of distance, and the observations have been carried out to nearly 250 million light-years where the red shifts correspond to velocities of recession of nearly 25,000 miles per second or 1/7 the velocity of light.

On this interpretation the present distribution of nebulae could be accounted for by the assumption that all the nebulae were once jammed together in a very small volume of space. Then, at a certain instant, some 1,800 million years ago, the jam exploded, the nebulae rushed outward in all directions with all possible velocities, and they have maintained these velocities to the present day. Thus the nebulae have now receded to various distances, depending upon their initial velocities, and our observations necessarily uncover the law of red shifts.

This pattern of history seems so remarkable that some observers view it with pardonable reserve, and try to imagine alternative explanations for the law of red shifts. Up to the present, they have failed. Other ways are known by which red shifts might be produced, but all of them introduce additional effects that should be conspicuous and actually are not found. Red shifts represent Doppler effects, physical recession of the nebulae, or the action of some hitherto unrecognized principle in nature.

COSMOLOGICAL THEORY

The preliminary sketch of the observable region was completed about ten years ago. It was not necessarily a finished picture, but it furnished a rough framework within which precise, detailed investigations could be planned with a proper understanding of their relation to the general scheme. Such new investigations, of course, were guided when practical by current theory. Let me explain the significance of this procedure.

Mathematicians deal with possible worlds, with an infinite number of logically consistent systems. Observers explore the one particular world we inhabit. Between the two stands the theorist. He studies possible worlds but only those which are compatible with the information furnished by observers. In other words, theory attempts to segregate the minimum number of possible worlds which must include the actual world we inhabit. Then the observer, with new factual information, attempts to reduce the list still further. And so it goes, observation and theory advancing together toward the common goal of science, knowledge of the structure and behavior of the physical universe.

The relation is evident in the history of cosmology. The study at first was pure speculation. But the exploration of space moved outward until finally a vast region, possibly a fair sample of the universe, was opened for inspection. Then theory was revitalized; it now had a sure base from which to venture forth.

Current theory starts with two fundamental principles:

general relativity and the cosmological principle. General relativity states that the geometry of space is determined by the contents of space, and formulates the nature of the relation. Crudely put, the principle states that space is curved in the vicinity of matter, and that the amount of curvature depends upon the amount of matter. Because of the irregular distribution of matter in our world, the small-scale structure of space is highly complex. However, if the universe is sufficiently homogeneous on the large scale, we may adopt a general curvature for the universe, or for the observable region as a whole, just as we speak of the general curvature of the earth's surface, disregarding the mountains and ocean basins. The nature of the spatial curvature, whether it is positive or negative, and the numerical value, is a subject for empirical investigation.

The second, or cosmological, principle is a pure assumption—the very simple postulate that, on the grand scale, the universe will appear much the same from whatever position it may be explored. In other words, there is no favored position in the universe, no center, no boundaries. If we, on the earth, see the universe expanding in all directions, then any other observer, no matter where he is located, will also see the universe expanding in the same manner. The postulate, it may be added, implies that, on the grand scale, the universe is homogeneous and isotropic—very much the same everywhere and in all directions.

Modern cosmological theory attempts to describe the types of universes that are compatible with the two principles, general relativity and the cosmological principle. Profound analysis of the problem leads to the following conclusions. Such universes are unstable. They might be momentarily in equilibrium, but the slightest internal disturbance would destroy the balance, and disturbances must occur. Therefore, these possible worlds are not stationary. They are, in general, either contracting or expanding, although theory in its present form does not indicate either the direction of change or the rate of change. At this point, the theorist turned to the reports of the observers. The empirical law of red shifts was accepted as visible evidence that the universe is expanding in a particular manner and at a known rate. Thus arose the conception of homogeneous expanding universes of general relativity.

In such universes, the spatial curvature is steadily diminishing as the expansion progresses. Furthermore, the nature of the expansion is such that gravitational assemblages maintain their identities. In other words, material bodies or groups and clusters of nebulae do not themselves expand but maintain their permanent dimensions as their neighbors recede from them in all directions.

Several types of expanding universes are possible, and some of them can be further specified by the nature of the curvature, whether it is positive or negative. In fact, the particular universe we inhabit could be identified if we had sufficiently precise information on three measurable quantities, namely, the rate of expansion, the mean density of matter in space, and the spatial curvature at the present epoch. Recent empirical investigations have been directed toward these problems, and the results will be briefly described in the remaining section of this discussion.

COMPARISON OF THEORY AND OBSERVATIONS

We may begin with two results which are thoroughly consistent with the theory. The first result concerns the assumption of homogeneity; the second, the conclusion that groups maintain their dimensions as the universe expands.

The distribution of nebulae has been studied in two ways. The first information came from sampling surveys at Mount Wilson and at the Lick Observatory. Small areas, systematically scattered over the sky, were studied with large telescopes. Thus the nebulae that were counted lay

in narrow cones penetrating to vast distances. These surveys established large-scale homogeneity over the three-
quarters of the sky that could be studied from the northern
latitudes of the observatories involved.

Later, the Harvard College Observatory, with the help of
its southern station, has furnished counts of nebulae extending over large areas but made with moderate-sized telescopes. In other words, these nebulae are scattered through
wide cones penetrating to moderate distances. Shapley, in
his reports, has stressed or perhaps overstressed, the familiar, small-scale irregularities of distribution, but analysis
of such published data as are adequately calibrated agrees
with the earlier conclusion. In fact, the mean results from
the two quite different methods of study are sensibly the
same. This fact reëmphasizes the large-scale homogeneity
of the observable region.

The second result is derived from a study of the Local
Group. Our own stellar system is one of a dozen nebulae that
form a loose group, more or less isolated in the general field.
These neighboring systems furnished the first clues to the
nature of the nebulae and the scale of internebular distances. They are so near that their brightest stars could be
recognized and compared with similar stars in our own system. Radial velocities of the members of the Local Group,
listed in Table I, suggest that the law of red shifts probably
does not operate within the group. This conclusion is positive evidence supporting the validity of the theory. If the
universe is expanding, the group maintains its dimensions
as the theory requires.

The remainder of the recently accumulated information
is not favorable to the theory. It is so damaging, in fact,
that the theory, in its present form, can be saved only by
assuming that the observational results include hidden systematic errors. The latter possibility will naturally persist
until the investigations can be repeated and improved.

Nevertheless, a careful reëxamination of the data now available suggests no adequate explanation of the discrepancies.

TABLE I

Radial Velocities in the Local Group

The observed velocities (second column) represent a more reasonable distribution than the velocities corrected for red shifts (fifth column). The latter are all large and negative with the exception of the first two, for which the red shifts are insignificant. This fact suggests that the law of red shifts does not operate within the Local Group.

LOCAL GROUP

Known members	Observed velocity	Distance in million light-years	Expected red shift	Velocity with red shift removed
L M C	+ 45	0.085	+ 13	+ 32
S M C	+ 13	0.095	+ 16	— 3
M 31	—130	0.7	+110	—240
NGC 6822	+ 20	0.5	+ 85	— 60
IC 1613*	...	1.3	+210	...
Fornax	— 40	0.6	+100	—140
Probable members				
NGC 6946	+ 90	1.6	+265	—175
NGC 1569	+ 60	2.3	+370	—310
IC 342	+ 30	2.3	+370	—340

* A spectrum of an object in IC 1613, obtained by Baade, shows a definitely negative velocity. The numerical value of the velocity is rather uncertain, and, for this reason is not included in the table. However, the negative sign indicates that IC 1613 is consistent with the other members of the Local Group.

THE INTERPRETATION OF RED SHIFTS

The investigations were designed to determine whether or not red shifts represent actual recession. In principle, the problem can be solved; a rapidly receding light source appears fainter than a similar but stationary source at the same momentary distance. The explanation of this well-known effect is quite simple when the beam of light is pictured as a stream of discrete quanta. Rapid recession thins out the stream of quanta, hence fewer quanta reach the eye per second, and the intensity, or rate of impact, is necessarily reduced. Quantitatively, the normal brightness is reduced by a fraction that is merely the velocity of recession divided by the velocity of light—in other words, the red shift expressed as a fraction of the normal wave lengths of the light in question. Recession at $\frac{1}{10}$ the velocity of light reduces the apparent brightness by 10 per cent; at $\frac{1}{4}$ the velocity of light, by 25 per cent.

For velocities of a few miles or a few hundred miles per second, the dimming factor is negligible. But for the extremely distant nebulae, where the apparent recessions reach tens of thousands of miles per second, the effects are large enough to be readily observed and measured. Hence, if the distances of nebulae were known quite accurately we could measure their apparent faintness and tell at once whether or not they are receding at the rates indicated by the red shifts.

Unfortunately, the problem is not so simple. The only general criterion of great distances is the very apparent faintness of the nebulae which we wish to test. Therefore, the proposed test involves a vicious circle, and the dimming factor merely leads to an error in distance. However, a possible escape from the vicious circle is found in the following procedure. Since the intrinsic luminosities of nebulae are known, their apparent faintness furnishes two scales of distances, depending upon whether we assume the nebulae to be stationary or receding. If, then, we analyze our data, if we map the observable region, using first one scale and then the other, we may find that the wrong scale leads to contradictions or at least to grave difficulties. Such attempts have been made and one scale does lead to trouble. It is the scale which includes the dimming factors of recession, which assumes that the universe is expanding.

ALTERNATIVE FORMS OF THE LAW OF RED SHIFTS

The project was carried out by the precise formulation of (a) the law of red shifts, and (b) the large-scale distribution of nebulae. The form of the law of red shifts is most readily derived from the study of the brightest nebulae in

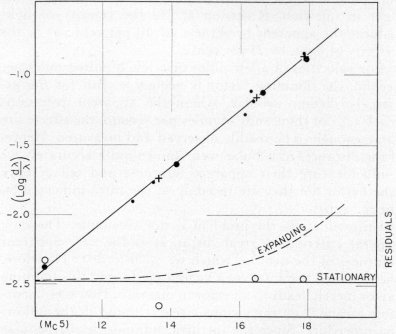

Fig. 14. The law of red shifts. The law of red shifts at very great distances is derived as a relation between apparent magnitudes of the fifth brightest members of clusters and the mean red shift observed in the clusters. The relation, log $d\lambda/\lambda =$ 0.2 m_5 + constant, shown as a full line in the diagram, indicates a linear law of red shifts ($d\lambda/\lambda =$ constant $\times$ Distance).

In the diagram, large discs represent clusters of high weight; dots, clusters of low weight; crosses, weighted means. Observed magnitudes have been corrected for all known effects (including the "energy effects," $3d\lambda/\lambda$), except recession factors. Thus, for a stationary universe, the law of red shifts is sensibly linear.

For an expanding universe, the recession factor would be applied, and the law would depart from the linear form. Such departures, shown by the broken curve, imply that the rate of expansion has been slowing down, and that the "age of the universe," the time since the expansion started, is less than 1,000 million years.

The diagram includes minor revisions of the observational data in accordance with recent investigations.

the great clusters. These nebulae, as a class, are the most luminous bodies in the universe, and their spectra can be

recorded out to the maximum distances. Furthermore, the
clusters are so similar that the apparent faintness of the 5 or

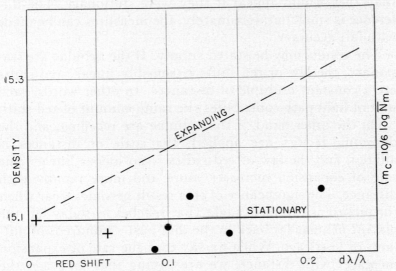

FIG. 15. Large-scale distribution of nebulae. If N_m is the number of nebulae per
square degree brighter than apparent magnitude m, then the average density (number
of nebulae divided by volume of space), in arbitrary units, is represented by (log
$N_m - 0.6$ m). Each point in the diagram represents a survey in which the observed
m have been corrected for all known effects (including the "energy effects," 3 $d\lambda/\lambda$)
but omitting the "recession factors," $d\lambda/\lambda$. The diagram indicates that for a stationary
universe, the density is independent of distance (or red shift).

If the universe were expanding, "recession factors" should be applied, and the
points would fall along the broken line, indicating that the density increases steadily
with distance. In order to escape this conclusion, it is necessary to introduce still
another effect such as spatial curvature which exactly compensates the recession
factors.

The dots represent surveys made at Mount Wilson and Mount Hamilton; the first
cross, the Shapley-Ames survey to m = 13±; the second cross, Harvard counts to
m = 17.5, extracted from *Proc. Nat. Acad.*, *24*, 148, 1938, and *26*, 166 and 554, 1940,
and reduced according to the procedure used in reducing the deeper surveys.

10 brightest members furnish reliable relative distances.
The observations now extend out to about 240 million light-
years where the red shift is about 13 per cent of the normal
wave lengths of the incoming light. Since the corresponding
velocity of recession is the same fraction of the velocity of

light, the nebulae in the most distant cluster observed, if they are actually receding, will appear 13 per cent fainter than they would appear if they were stationary. The difference is small but, fortunately, the measures can be made with fair accuracy.

The results may be stated simply. If the nebulae are stationary, the law of red shifts is sensibly linear; red shifts are a constant multiple of distances. In other words, each unit of light path contributes the same amount of red shift.

On the other hand, if the nebulae are receding, and the dimming factors are applied, the scale of distances is altered, and the law of red shifts is no longer linear. The rate of expansion increases more and more rapidly with distance. The significance of this result becomes clear when the picture is reversed. Light that reaches us today left the distant nebulae far back in the dim past—hundreds of millions of years ago. When we say that the rate of expansion increases with distance, we are saying that long ago the universe was expanding much faster than it is today; that, for the last several hundred million years at least, the rate of expansion has been slowing down. Therefore, the so-called "age of the universe," the time interval since the expansion began, is much shorter than the 1,800 million years suggested by a linear law of red shifts. If the measures are reliable, the interval would be less than 1,000 million years—a fraction of the age of the earth and comparable with the history of life on the earth. The nature of the expansion is permissible and, in fact, specifies certain types of possible worlds. But the time scale is probably not acceptable. Either the measures are unreliable or red shifts do not represent expansion of the universe.

THE LARGE-SCALE DISTRIBUTION OF NEBULAE

If the new formulation of the law of red shifts were unsupported by other evidence, the implications would probably be disregarded. But similar discrepancies are met in quite independent studies of large-scale distribution. Five sampling surveys (four at Mount Wilson and one at Mount Hamilton) made with large reflectors, furnish the numbers of nebulae per unit area in the sky, to successive limits of apparent faintness. The results furnish the numbers of nebulae per unit volume in five spheres whose radii range from about 155 to 420 million light-years on the stationary distance scale, or about 145 to 365 million light-years for the expanding distance scale.

On the assumption that red shifts do not represent actual recession, the large-scale distribution is sensibly homogeneous—the average number of nebulae per unit volume of space is much the same for each of the spheres. Further confirmation is found in some of the recent Harvard counts of nebulae which fall within the area of the sky covered by the deep surveys, and which are based on the same scale of apparent faintness. Sufficient data can be extracted from the reports to determine a mean density over large areas extending out to perhaps 100 million light-years, and the result is in substantial agreement with those of the earlier investigations. All of these data lead to the very simple conception of a sensibly infinite homogeneous universe of which the observable region is an insignificant sample.

The inclusion of dimming corrections for recession, because they alter the scale of distance in a nonlinear way, necessarily destroys the homogeneity. The number of nebulae per unit volume now appears to increase systematically with distance in all directions. The result violates the cosmological principle of no favored position and, consequently, is referred to some neglected factor in the calculations. If the density appeared to diminish outward, we would at once suspect the presence of internebular obscuration, or, perhaps, the existence of a supersystem of nebulae. But an apparently increasing density offers a much more serious problem. About the only known, permissible interpretation is found in positive spatial curvature, which, by a sort of optical foreshortening, would crowd the observed nebulae into apparently smaller and smaller volumes of space as the distance increased.

Spatial curvature is an expected feature of an expanding universe, and, together with the precise form of the law of red shifts, further specifies a particular type of possible world. Thus, if the measures were reliable, we might conclude that the initial cosmological problem had been solved; that now we knew the nature of the universe we inhabit. But the situation is not so simple. Just as the departures from linearity in the law of red shifts indicate a universe that is strangely young, so the apparent departures from homogeneity indicate a universe that is strangely small and dense.

The sign of the curvature required to restore homogeneity is positive, hence the universe is "closed"; it has a finite volume although, of course, there are no boundaries. The amount of curvature indicates the volume of the universe: about four times the volume of the observable region. Such a universe would contain perhaps 400 million nebulae. The total mass, however, would be far greater than that which can be attributed to the nebulae alone.

CONCLUSION

Thus the use of dimming corrections leads to a particular kind of universe, but one which most students are likely to reject as highly improbable. Furthermore, the strange features of this universe are merely the dimming corrections expressed in different terms. Omit the dimming factors, and the oddities vanish. We are left with the simple, even familiar, concept of a sensibly infinite universe. All the difficulties are transferred to the interpretation of red shifts which cannot then be the familiar velocity shifts.

Two further points may be mentioned. In the first place, the reference of red shifts to some hitherto unknown principle does not in any way destroy the validity of the theory of expanding universes. It merely removes the theory from immediate contact with observations. We may still suppose that the universe is either expanding or contracting, but at a rate so slow that it cannot now be disentangled from the gross effects of the superposed red shifts.

Secondly, the conclusions drawn from the empirical investigations involve the assumptions that the measures are reliable and the data are representative. These questions have been carefully reëxamined during the past few years. Various minor revisions have been made, but the end-results remain substantially unchanged. By the usual criteria of probable errors, the data seem to be sufficiently consistent for their purpose. Nevertheless, the operations are delicate, and the most significant data are found near the limits of the greatest telescopes. Under such conditions, it is always possible that the results may be affected by hidden systematic errors. Although no suggestion of such errors has been found, the possibility will persist until the investigations can be repeated with improved techniques and more powerful telescopes. Ultimately, the problem should be settled beyond question by the 200-inch reflector destined for Palomar. The range of that telescope and the corresponding ranges of the dimming corrections should be about twice those examined in the present investigations. Factors of 25 per cent in the apparent brightness of nebulae at the limits of the spectrograph and 40 to 50 per cent at the limits of direct photography should be unmistakable if they really exist.

Meanwhile, on the basis of the evidence now available, apparent discrepancies between theory and observation must be recognized. A choice is presented, as once before in the days of Copernicus, between a strangely small, finite universe and a sensibly infinite universe plus a new principle of nature.

For References see p. 297.

III

ENERGY PRODUCTION IN STARS

By HANS A. BETHE

Cornell University

THE sun continuously releases enormous quantities of radiation into space. Each second the energy of the emitted radiation amounts to 4×10^{33} ergs. At the rate of one cent per kilowatt-hour, we should have to pay a billion billion dollars to keep the sun going for a single second.

Terrestrial sources of energy are ridiculously insignificant in comparison with these huge amounts. Even if we assumed (which we know to be false) that the sun consisted entirely of coal (carbon), mixed with the right quantity of oxygen, the combustion of that entire material would supply the sun's energy for only 2,500 years, which is less than the duration of the written history of mankind.

We know, however, from radioactive measurements* that the age of the earth is at least 1,500 million years. The sun is likely to be at least as old, and there is no reason to assume that its radiation 1,500 million years ago was much less than it is now. In fact, it is certain that the radiation did not change appreciably during the last 500 million years, because during all this time life existed on earth. Life and the chemical substances on which it is based, like proteins and water and many others, can exist only in a fairly narrow temperature range—approximately between $-50°$ and $+60°$ C. To have kept the earth's temperature

---

* Radioactivity provides a kind of geological sand clock. It is known from laboratory experiments that uranium, the parent element of the most important radioactive family, spontaneously changes into lead at such a rate that one-half of the uranium originally present is transformed in 4.6 billion years. Measuring the lead contained in a specimen of uranium ore, it is possible to deduce the age of that ore.

within this temperature range, the sun's radiation must
have been approximately what it is at the present time.

THEORIES OF STELLAR ENERGY

Any acceptable theory of the source of stellar energy must
explain two things: first, the enormous rate of production
of energy and, second, the long period of time over which
the sun is known to have been emitting energy.

Most of the older theories failed because they did not provide a sufficiently large energy reservoir and, therefore, did
not give a sufficiently long lifetime. Historically, the first
theory which can be taken seriously was Helmholtz' contraction hypothesis. According to this, the sun and all stars
began as very large and dilute bodies, and have constantly
gotten smaller due to gravitational forces; they fall, so to
speak, toward their own center. The energy set free by this
"fall" is converted into heat, just as in the case of a falling
stone, and the heat energy in turn into radiation. This
hypothesis gives the correct *rate* of energy production as
can be shown from the general theory of Eddington. But
even if the sun started with an infinite diameter, the energy
set free during the contraction to its present size would only
be sufficient for 30 million years at the present rate of radiation. That length of time seemed sufficient in Helmholtz'
day when the age of the earth was believed to be only of the
order of a few tens of millions of years. But the discovery of
radioactivity showed that much longer times were involved,
and thus disproved the contraction theory.

Radioactivity itself seemed to offer a more abundant
source of energy. Indeed, there would be no difficulty about
the time-scale in this case, since uranium keeps radiating
with almost undiminished intensity for 4,000 million years.
However, in order to explain the *rate* of radiation, one
would have to assume that the sun consisted entirely of
uranium. This is an absurd assumption; terrestrial and

meteoric evidence would indicate a uranium content of about one part in a million, an amount entirely insignificant for the energy production. Moreover, some stars are known to emit a thousand times more radiation per gram of their mass than does the sun, and it would be obviously impossible to explain that rate of radiation by radioactive processes.

The theory most widely believed in the nineteen-twenties was Eddington's hypothesis that the energy was produced by a mutual annihilation of protons and electrons in which the mass energy, mc^2, of these particles was converted into radiation. Such a process would certainly give sufficient energy; in fact, it gives a greater energy and, therefore, a longer lifetime than any other conceivable process. However, no such process has ever been observed, and there is no theoretical reason to believe in its occurrence. Moreover, *if* it occurred, it would be almost impossible to understand why it should happen in the interior of stars any more than on earth, and why it should depend strongly on the internal temperature of the star, as the energy production is known to do.

The way for the actual solution of the problem of energy production was opened when Rutherford discovered, in 1919, the transmutation of atomic nuclei. About 1930 Atkinson and Houtermans suggested that such transmutations might be the source of stellar energy. It can easily be shown that nuclear reactions would give sufficient energy and would also fulfill the other requirements for an acceptable theory. Therefore most astronomers and physicists accepted the nuclear reaction hypothesis in principle even before the actual reactions responsible for the energy production were found. Today we have a consistent picture of the energy production, based on nuclear reactions. In order to understand this theory we have to study the physics of the atomic nucleus.

THE ATOMIC NUCLEUS

Each atom consists of a nucleus which is positively charged and a number of negatively charged electrons going around it. The diameter of the nucleus is less than 1/10,000 of the diameter of the atom, yet the nucleus contains practically all the mass of the atom. Each nucleus, in turn, is known to consist of neutrons and protons. A *proton* is the nucleus of the hydrogen atom, the lightest nucleus known; it carries a positive charge, $+e$, which is numerically equal to the charge of the electron. A *neutron* is a particle without charge (electrically neutral) whose mass is very slightly greater than that of the proton.

If a nucleus contains N neutrons and Z protons, its charge will be $+Ze$ and its mass will be approximately $N + Z$ times the mass of the proton. Z is known as the *atomic number;* it is equal to the number of electrons in the neutral atom and determines the chemical properties of the element. We know elements with Z ranging from 1 to 92, $Z = 1$ being hydrogen and $Z = 92$, the heaviest element, uranium. All of these elements, with the exception of four (namely, $Z = 43, 61, 85, 87$), are found in nature; the excepted four can be produced only in the laboratory.

$N + Z = A$ is called the *mass number* of the nucleus; it is approximately equal to the well-known atomic weight, M. For most elements, there exist two or more nuclei with different mass numbers A; these are called *isotopes.* One of the oldest known examples is chlorine, $Z = 17$, which has two isotopes, $A = 35$ and 37. To distinguish isotopes, physicists put the mass number as an upperscript on the chemical symbol for the element like this: Cl^{35}, pronounced "chlorine 35." Frequently, the atomic number Z is also attached on the upper left-hand corner, thus: $^{17}Cl^{35}$; this is really unnecessary because Z is uniquely determined by the chemical symbol, but it is convenient for the reader. Natural chlorine contains about 75 per cent of the lighter, and 25 per cent of the heavier, isotope. The chemical properties, being determined by Z, are the same for the two isotopes of Cl, and it requires the most refined methods of modern chemistry and physics to separate them from each other. However, from the standpoint of nuclear physics, the two isotopes are totally different; the $^{17}Cl^{35}$ nucleus contains 17 protons and 18 neutrons, whereas $^{17}Cl^{37}$ contains 17 protons and 20 neutrons.

A nucleus is completely characterized by its atomic number and its mass number. But further information about the nucleus is furnished by the *atomic weight*, M. The atomic weight is defined as the mass of the atom (nucleus with Z electrons around it) in terms of the mass of the atom O^{16} which* is arbitrarily put equal to 16.000000. The atomic weights of some of the important light atoms based on the latest measurements are given in Table I.

TABLE I

Atomic Weights of Light Atoms

Name	Symbol	Z	N	A	M
Electron	ϵ	..	..	0	0.000 549
Neutron	n	0	1	1	1.008 93
Hydrogen	H^1	1	0	1	1.008 123
Deuterium	H^2	1	1	2	2.014 708
Helium	He^4	2	2	4	4.003 90
Lithium 7	Li^7	3	4	7	7.018 22
Boron 10	B^{10}	5	5	10	10.016 18
Boron 11	B^{11}	5	6	11	11.012 84
Carbon 12	C^{12}	6	6	12	12.003 82
Carbon 13	C^{13}	6	7	13	13.007 51
Nitrogen 13	N^{13}	7	6	13	13.009 88
Nitrogen 14	N^{14}	7	7	14	14.007 51
Nitrogen 15	N^{15}	7	8	15	15.004 89
Oxygen 15	O^{15}	8	7	15	15.007 8
Oxygen 16	O^{16}	8	8	16	16.000 000

Z = atomic number = number of protons.   A = mass number = N + Z.
N = number of neutrons in nucleus.   M = atomic weight.

* In the customary scale of atomic weights used in chemistry, the atomic weight of natural oxygen is put equal to 16. Since oxygen consists of the isotopes 16, 17, 18, with the last two being very rare, the chemical scale differs slightly (by about 1 part in 4,000) from the physical atomic weights scale used here.

It will be noticed from Table I that the masses of the hydrogen atom and of the neutron are slightly greater than 1. Therefore, if we put 8 protons and 8 neutrons together to form an O^{16} nucleus, we should expect a mass somewhat greater than 16 units. Actually the atomic weight of O^{16} is exactly 16. Where did the remaining mass go to? Here the (special) relativity theory gives the answer: The smaller mass of O^{16} indicates that this nucleus contains less energy than the 16 separate protons and neutrons. Energy is set free when the protons and neutrons combine to form a nucleus; in fact, this is the reason why a nucleus stays together at all. The amount of energy set free, the binding energy, can be calculated from the decrease of mass. According to the relativity theory, a decrease of mass by m corresponds to a decrease of energy by mc^2 where c is the velocity of light. One unit of atomic weight is easily calculated to correspond to 0.0015 ergs of energy. Then from Table I we find:

	Mass of 8 neutrons	8.0714
	Mass of 8 hydrogen atoms	8.0650
	Total	16.1364
Minus	Mass of O^{16} atom	16.0000
	Mass change	0.1364
	Corresponding energy change	0.000205 ergs $=$ 205 microergs

$$(1 \text{ microerg} = \tfrac{1}{1.000.000} \text{ of an erg})$$

This energy may seem very small, but it must be remembered that it is for a single oxygen nucleus! If we could produce a *gram* of oxygen nuclei by bringing half a gram of protons and half a gram of neutrons together, the energy set free would be $7.7 \cdot 10^{18}$ ergs, or 210,000 kilowatt-hours. The ordinary combustion of a gram of coal gives about $\frac{1}{100}$ of a kilowatt-hour. Thus it is seen what tremendous energies are liberated when nuclei are formed from protons and neutrons: a very promising result when we are trying to explain the energy production in stars.

Most of the nuclei occurring in nature are stable, that is, they will exist forever unless they have a violent collision with another nucleus. But there are some which are radioactive; if they are left to themselves, they will, after a shorter or longer time, emit some particle and thereby transform into another type of nucleus. Two such radioactive nuclei are listed in Table I, N^{13} and O^{15}. For example, the nucleus in N^{13} changes over into C^{13} when it undergoes a radioactive transformation. This means that the total number of nuclear particles in the nucleus remains unchanged, equal to 13, but the charge decreases from 7e to 6e. Therefore the radioactive process must consist of the emission of a particle with the charge $+e$ which has a very small mass: small compared with the mass of the proton. We know a particle of very small mass, the electron, whose mass is only $1/1.840$ of the mass of the proton. However, at first sight there appears to be a difficulty because the electron has a charge $-e$. Fortunately, there exists another variety of electron, the positive electron, discovered by Anderson, which has a charge $+e$ and is otherwise entirely similar to the ordinary, negative electron. This positive electron does not exist in ordinary matter, it is only formed in cosmic radiation and emitted by radioactive nuclei, such as N^{13} and O^{15}. After its emission it will travel a certain short distance and then will "die," combining with an ordinary, negative electron. In this "annihilation of an electron pair" an energy of $2mc^2$ is set free where m is the mass of one electron; this energy is converted into radiation of very short wave length.

There are also many radioactive nuclei that emit ordinary negative electrons. Table II gives a list of all known isotopes of the first 9 elements, including both the stable and the radioactive ones. Ordinarily, for each element, the radioactive isotopes are grouped around the stable ones; those which are heavier than the stable isotopes emit negative electrons, whereas the lighter radioactive isotopes emit positive electrons.

TABLE II

Name	Symbol	Z	Mass numbers of stable isotopes	Radioactive isotopes emitting positive electrons	negative electrons
Neutron	n	0	...	...	1
Hydrogen	H	1	1, 2	...	3
Helium	He	2	3, 4	...	6
Lithium	Li	3	6, 7	...	8
Beryllium	Be	4	9	(7)*	10
Boron	B	5	10, 11	...	12
Carbon	C	6	12, 13	10, 11	14
Nitrogen	N	7	14, 15	13	16
Oxygen	O	8	16, 17, 18	15	19
Fluorine	F	9	19	17, 18	20

* Captures negative electrons but does not emit positive ones.

The lifetime of the known radioactive nuclei varies widely, from $\frac{1}{50}$ second to about 10^{11} years. However, the two radioactive nuclei which are of importance for the energy production in stars, N^{13} and O^{15}, have very moderate lifetimes, namely, 10 minutes and 2 minutes, respectively.

Almost every mass number A is represented by at least one nucleus, either stable or radioactive. For instance, there are 3 different nuclei with A$=$10, namely, a radioactive isotope of beryllium, a stable one of boron, and a radioactive one of carbon (Table II). There is only one mass number for which no nucleus exists at all, namely, 5. It is true that $^2He^5$ is formed in certain nuclear reactions, but it disintegrates immediately into $^2He^4$ and a neutron. "Immediately" means within about 10^{-20} seconds, in contrast to a radioactive nucleus like N^{13} which lives for about 10 minutes. The immediate decay of the He^5 is due to the fact that there is no binding force between He^4 and a neutron. Similarly there is no binding force between $^2He^4$ and a proton so that the nucleus $^3Li^5$ does not hold together either. As will be shown later, this is quite important for astrophysics.

NUCLEAR TRANSMUTATIONS

After having presented a general idea of the structure of nuclei, we may now discuss nuclear transmutations or reactions. In many respects nuclear transmutations are similar to chemical reactions: the neutron and the proton are the nuclear analogues of the chemical elements, the nuclei, the analogues of chemical compounds, and the transmutation consists in a reshuffling of the neutrons and protons between two nuclei. There are two types of nuclear transmutations, the *simple capture* and the *particle reaction*.

In the simple capture, two nuclei which come into contact simply combine. The resulting nucleus contains all the neutrons and protons of the reacting nuclei. This simple capture is always possible provided the resulting nucleus exists at all.* An example of simple capture is the nuclear reaction

$$^3\text{Li}^7 + {}^1\text{H}^1 = {}^4\text{Be}^8 + \gamma; \tag{1}$$

in this a lithium nucleus of mass number 7 combines with a proton to give a beryllium nucleus of mass 8, the excess energy being transformed into a γ-ray. If the reacting nuclei ($^3\text{Li}^7$ and $^1\text{H}^1$) are given, it is easy to find out which nucleus will be formed by simple capture; the resulting nucleus must contain all the protons of the reacting nuclei, namely, $3 + 1 = 4$, and must therefore be beryllium, the fourth element of the periodic table. It must also contain all the neutrons of the reactants, and therefore its mass number must equal the sum of the mass numbers of the reactants, which is $7 + 1 = 8$.

In a particle reaction, the neutrons and protons of the reacting nuclei are not all combined in one nucleus, but are redistributed among the two new nuclei. A proton col-

---

* Since $^2\text{He}^5$ and $^3\text{Li}^5$ do not exist, $^2\text{He}^4$ can capture neither a neutron nor a proton.

liding with a Li^7 nucleus does not always give rise to reaction (1) but may also yield two He^4 nuclei:

$$^3Li^7 + {}^1H^1 = {}^2He^4 + {}^2He^4 \qquad (2)$$

Again, in particle reactions, all neutrons and protons of the reacting nuclei must appear in the products. Therefore, the sum of the left superscripts (atomic numbers) must be the same on the two sides of the equation (in our case $3 + 1 = 2 + 2$), and the same is true of the right superscripts (mass numbers, $7 + 1 = 4 + 4$).

In any nuclear reaction, some energy is set free or absorbed. For instance, to find the energy set free in reaction (2), we need only calculate the mass difference between the nuclei on the left and on the right side of the equation. Consulting Table I, we have

$$
\begin{array}{rl}
\text{Mass of } {}^3Li^7 = & 7.01822 \\
\text{Mass of } {}^1H^1 = & 1.00812 \\
\hline
\text{Sum} \quad & 8.02634 \\
\text{Mass of 2 atoms of } {}^2He^4 = & 8.00780 \\
\hline
\text{Mass difference} = & 0.01854 \\
\end{array}
$$

Corresponding energy 27.8 microergs.

This energy must be disposed of, and the manner of its disposal is considerably different for particle reactions and simple capture. In particle reactions, energy is transformed into kinetic energy of the two nuclei formed in the reaction. For example, the two $^2He^4$ nuclei produced in reaction (2) fly in opposite directions with a speed of about 12,500 miles per second. In simple capture reactions, it is not possible to dispose of the energy in this way: the single nucleus formed cannot fly away from itself.* The energy must therefore be carried away in another form, and this form is electromagnetic radiation. Therefore in each simple capture reaction a

* The velocity of this nucleus after the reaction is completely determined by the law of conservation of momentum.

quantum of radiation (γ-ray) is emitted. In particle reactions, no radiation is emitted except in extremely rare cases.

Nuclear reactions are reversible, thus the reaction (2) can also go from left to right. However, for this to occur, the two helium nuclei must hit each other with a relative velocity of $2 \cdot 12{,}500 = 25{,}000$ miles per second, in order that sufficient energy be available to form the nuclei Li^7 and H^1 whose combined mass (and therefore energy) is much higher than that of the two He^4 nuclei. Such "endothermic" reactions can, therefore, not occur in the interior of stars where the atomic nuclei move around with velocities of "only" about 500 miles per second.

It has been shown theoretically and experimentally that particle reactions are much more probable than simple capture whenever both can occur. $Li^7 + H^1$ will react according to equation (1) in perhaps one case of 10,000; in all other cases reaction (2) will take place. However, there are many instances in which no particle reaction can occur because a large amount of energy is required, as in the case of the collision of two He^4 nuclei. Then simple capture will be the only remaining possibility.

The radioactive decay which was discussed above is a spontaneous process; its rate cannot be influenced by external conditions, such as temperature, density, or the presence of other nuclei. On the other hand, the nuclear transmutations depend on the contact of two nuclei. The frequency of their occurrence will, therefore, increase with the density of the material. Moreover, there are strong forces opposing the approach of two nuclei. Since all nuclei are positively charged, there is an electric repulsion between them. Only if they approach each other with great velocity will it be possible for them to overcome the electric repulsion and to come into contact. According to the laws of classical mechanics, a proton must have a kinetic energy of about 3 microergs to penetrate to a carbon nucleus. Actually, quantum mechanics predicts that the penetration is also possible at lower energies, but the probability of the penetration decreases rapidly with decreasing kinetic energy of the proton.

The probability of penetration, and therefore of a nuclear reaction, has been calculated by Gamow, Condon, and Gurney. If two nuclei of charges $Z_1 e$ and $Z_2 e$ collide with a relative velocity v, then the probability of occurrence of a nuclear reaction is

$$\eta = \Gamma \epsilon^{-\dfrac{4\pi^2 Z_1 Z_2 e^2}{hv}} \tag{3}$$

where ϵ is the base of the natural logarithms (2.718 . . .), h is Planck's constant and Γ a coefficient which depends on the particular reaction in question, that is, on whether it is a particle reaction or a simple capture, on the diameters of the reacting nuclei, etc. The most important term for our problem is, however, the exponential function. This function becomes extremely small for low velocity of the colliding nuclei. It is therefore clear that we cannot hope to "tap" the large energies contained in atomic nuclei unless particles of high kinetic energy are already present to begin with.

In the laboratory nuclear transmutations are produced by accelerating a *few particles* to quite *high kinetic energies*. This acceleration is done electrically; a tension of 500,000 volts gives a proton a kinetic energy of about 0.8 microerg. Such an amount of kinetic energy gives the proton an appreciable probability of penetrating into a carbon nucleus and causing a transmutation. However, out of a million accelerated protons there will still be only one which will make a successful hit; the others will be slowed down by collisions with atoms without producing transmutations, and their kinetic energy will be lost (transformed into heat). Since the energy set free in nuclear transmutations is only of the order of 10 microergs per process, it is obviously impracticable to use nuclear transmutations to produce energy in the laboratory; perhaps 100,000 times more energy is necessary to accelerate a million protons than is set free in the one transmutation that is obtained.

Another characteristic of laboratory experiments on nuclear transmutations is the extremely small number of particles accelerated. In the big cyclotron* of Dr. E. O. Lawrence at Berkeley, California, only 0.1 milligram of protons goes through the machine in a whole day's work.

In stars, we have just the opposite case. Owing to the high temperatures in the interior, all the protons in the sun have high kinetic energies—there are a billion billion billion tons of fast protons. Moreover, they have these high energies all the time; they are not slowed down by collisions with other atoms because all atoms have equally high energies. Therefore the efficiency of the energy production will be much better; every nuclear transmutation that occurs gives a net gain of energy because it is no longer necessary to shoot a million projectiles at the target in order to have one hit. Thus energy can be produced by nuclear transmutations in the intense heat inside of stars, whereas it cannot be produced in the terrestrial laboratory.

On the other hand, the kinetic energies of the nuclei in stars are very small compared with those used in the laboratory. It is true that the temperature is about 20,000,000° C. at the center of the sun, and the atomic nuclei are therefore traveling with much greater speed than the molecules of the air in our room. However, their average kinetic energy is still only about 0.004 microergs: 200 times smaller than the energies commonly used in the laboratory. Again it is true that some particles in a hot gas have much higher energies than the average, but there are very few indeed which have more than 10 times the average energy, and this

* See E. O. Lawrence, "Atoms, New and Old," *Science in Progress,* I.

is still about 20 times less than the energies used in the laboratory.

Thus we find that the transmutations in stars are produced by very many nuclei of relatively small kinetic energy, in the laboratory by very few of high kinetic energy. It is this difference of conditions that is mainly responsible for the uncertainties that still exist regarding the probability of nuclear transmutations in stars.

The value of the constant Γ in equation (3) must be deduced from laboratory experiments, and the formula must then be used to calculate the reaction rate in the interior of stars. Apart from uncertainties in the velocity of the particles in the interior of stars, it is known that equation (3) is not always quite exact. Therefore it must be expected that our estimates of the reaction rates may be wrong by a factor 5 or 10 either way.

THE CARBON CYCLE

Which of the nuclear transmutations are responsible for the energy production in stars? To answer this question, we may be guided by the Gamow-Condon-Gurney formula (3). Since we are concerned with particles of relatively low velocity v, our only hope to obtain an appreciable reaction probability consists in choosing the product of the charges of the reacting nuclei Z_1 and Z_2 very small. This suggests taking one of the charges equal to one, the smallest possible value,* which means taking a proton as one of the reacting nuclei. There are other strong reasons for choosing protons: Hydrogen is by far the most abundant element in stars, there being at least 5 hydrogen atoms to every atom of another kind in the sun. Furthermore, at any given temperature, protons travel faster than any other kind of nuclei,

* Neutrons which have no charge can be excluded because they cannot exist in the presence of other atomic nuclei for more than a small fraction of a second without being captured.

which again increases the probability of a nuclear reaction, according to equation (3).

The other nucleus which reacts with the proton should also have a small charge, Z. However, it is not possible to have for the second nucleus another proton, because the combination of two protons would give the nucleus $^2He^2$, which certainly does not exist. Similarly, the second nucleus cannot be He^4 because, as shown above, this nucleus cannot capture protons owing to the nonexistence of the nucleus $^3Li^5$. If Li^5 existed, the capture of protons by helium would be a most important reaction in stars.

The first element which can react with a proton is lithium. The most common reaction between Li^7 and H^1 is reaction (2) which as noted above was found to liberate a very large amount of energy. Unfortunately, the amounts of lithium in the sun and other stars are very small, so that the energy supply would only last for a short time. Moreover, if we use formula (3) to calculate the rate of reaction (2) at a temperature of 20,000,000° C., it will be found that all the lithium will be consumed in about a minute. Therefore all the lithium which may have been in the interior of the sun must have been consumed long ago, presumably at a time when the interior was not yet as hot as it is now. Reaction (2) converts the lithium into helium and thus makes it disappear forever. A similar situation is found for beryllium (Z=4) and boron (Z=5). Both of them can be safely assumed to have disappeared from the interior of the sun and similar stars.

Quite different transmutations occur when the next element, carbon, reacts with protons. By inspection of the atomic weights of the nuclei concerned, one can easily see that no particle reaction is energetically possible between C^{12} and protons. In particular, the reaction which would correspond to (2), that is,

$$^6C^{12} + {}^1H^1 = {}^5B^9 + {}^2He^4$$

can only take place if the protons have a kinetic energy of about 10 microergs. This is about 1,000 times the kinetic energy of the protons actually existing in stars. Therefore the only possible reaction is simple capture, as follows:

$$_6C^{12} + {}_1H^1 = {}_7N^{13} + \gamma \qquad\qquad (A)$$

the γ indicating the emission of a γ-ray. The nucleus formed in the carbon reaction (A) is a well-known radioactive nucleus which will decay spontaneously with the emission of a positive electron

$$_7N^{13} = {}_6C^{13} + \epsilon^+ \qquad\qquad (B)$$

The remaining nucleus, C^{13}, is stable and accordingly will live until it is hit by another proton. Again, all conceivable particle reactions are ruled out because they would consume energy, and we get another simple capture:

$$_6C^{13} + {}_1H^1 = {}_7N^{14} + \gamma \qquad\qquad (C)$$

N^{14} is another stable nucleus, so we get the further reactions,

$$_7N^{14} + {}_1H^1 = {}_8O^{15} + \gamma \qquad\qquad (D)$$
$$_8O^{15} = {}_7N^{15} + \epsilon^+ \qquad\qquad (E)$$

The nucleus N^{15} will again be stable until it reacts with a proton. However, this time the result is different: There *is* a particle reaction which is energetically possible, namely,

$$_7N^{15} + {}_1H^1 = {}_6C^{12} + {}_2He^4 \qquad\qquad (F)$$

According to Table I, the two nuclei on the left are heavier than those on the right by 0.00529 mass units so that an energy of 7.9 microergs is set free in the reaction. Because (F) is a particle reaction, it is much more probable than the simple capture,

$$_7N^{15} + {}_1H^1 = {}_8O^{16} + \gamma$$

Experimental data indicate that this simple capture occurs only once in about 100,000 cases.

The six reactions (A) to (F) are very remarkable. It will be seen that the nucleus carbon 12, which is the starting point of our reaction chain, is reproduced in the last reaction. "Carbon is the phoenix which is burnt six times and finally rises from its ashes." The importance of the carbon cycle is largely due to this reproduction of the carbon: the process does not use up the carbon nuclei, which are relatively rare in the sun, and therefore it can continue for a long time in contrast to the reactions involving Li, Be, or B.

The net effect of the carbon cycle, as can be seen from the equations, is the consumption of four protons and the production of one $^2He^4$ nucleus (α-particle) and two positive electrons. The latter are known to combine with ordinary (negative) electrons giving two γ-rays. Therefore, altogether we obtain the combination of four protons and two negative electrons into an α-particle. This combination could not occur directly by a "meeting" of the six particles concerned because the probability for such an event is practically zero. In fact, it can easily be calculated that such an event has probably not occurred even once during the entire life of the sun. The carbon is required as a catalyst to make the building up of the α-particles possible. But the actual "fuel" is hydrogen, and this is very fortunate because hydrogen is the most abundant element in the stars. Therefore the stars utilize the fuel which they have in the greatest supply.

The energy set free in a complete carbon cycle can be calculated from the masses of hydrogen and helium. We have:

Mass of 4 hydrogen atoms (4 protrons + 4 electrons)	4.03250
Mass of helium atom (helium nucleus + 2 electrons)	4.00390
Difference (difference between the mass of 4 protrons + 2 electrons, and that of a helium nucleus)	0.02860 mass units,

corresponding to 43 microergs. A small fraction of this energy (3 microergs) goes into "neutrinos" and is not recoverable. The remainder goes into radiation which is finally emitted from the sun.

It should be said at this point that the radiation which we see has nothing to do with the γ-rays emitted in the "simple capture" reactions. The γ-rays have wave lengths about a million times shorter than the visible radiation coming from the sun. In fact, the γ-rays will not travel very far before they are absorbed by an electron; this electron thereby acquires a large kinetic energy and subsequently loses this energy again by emitting, successively, several quanta of light of lower frequency and therefore lower quantum energy $h\nu$. The same process is repeated again, until the energy of the original light quantum is subdivided into about 1,000 quanta of lesser energy. These quanta are still continually absorbed by electrons and reëmitted; on the average, a light quantum in the sun travels less than a centimeter before it is absorbed. At any point in the interior of the sun, large numbers of light quanta travel in all directions; but there is a small excess of quanta moving outward; in this way the energy is transported to the surface. If a quantum could be followed on its way out (this is actually not possible because after each absorption and reëmission a different quantum is emitted) we should find it going back and forth many times until, after several thousand years, it would come to the surface of the sun and be emitted into space.

We have found that about 40 microergs are set free for each helium nucleus produced in the sun, or 10 for each proton destroyed. One gram of the sun's material has been calculated to contain about $2 \cdot 10^{23}$ protons. Therefore if all the protons can be converted into helium, the available energy supply is $2 \cdot 10^{18}$ ergs per gram. At present the sun radiates about 2 ergs per gram of its mass. At this rate the energy supply will last for about 30 billion years. *It is evi-*

dent that our nuclear reactions represent a sufficiently plentiful source of energy.

RATE OF ENERGY PRODUCTION

How does the *rate* of energy production come out of our theory? Here we must rely on laboratory experiments, on formula (3), and on the value for the temperature at the center of the sun calculated by astrophysicists on the basis of Eddington's theory. Using this information, we can calculate how long any nucleus at the center of the sun will live, on the average, before it is attacked by a proton and undergoes a nuclear transmutation. If this calculation is made for a temperature of 20,000,000° C., we find for the average lifetime of

C^{12}	2,500,000	years
N^{13}	10	minutes (spontaneous decay)
C^{13}	50,000	years
N^{14}	4,000,000	years
O^{15}	2	minutes (spontaneous decay)
N^{15}	20	years

A complete cycle of the 6 reactions (A) to (F) takes, therefore, about 6,000,000 years, or, as one newspaper reporter once wrote, 6,550,020 years and 12 minutes. All our figures are uncertain by about a factor of 10 either way.

The amount of carbon and nitrogen in stars has been estimated by astrophysicists to be between 1 and 10 per cent by weight, the most recent estimates favoring the higher figure. This would mean that in each gram of material at the center of the sun about 25 million carbon nuclei capture a proton every second, which means that the energy developed is 1,000 ergs per gram per second. It must be remembered that the outer regions of the sun are much cooler than the center and therefore contribute very little to the energy production. On the average, over the entire sun, the theoretical production comes out to be about 30 ergs per second per gram of the sun's mass. Although the observed radiation is only 2 ergs per gram per second, the agreement with theory is quite satisfactory in view of the many uncertainties in the calculations.

In order to see this result in the right perspective, we may calculate the theoretical rate of energy production if other reactions than the carbon cycle are assumed to be responsible for the energy production. If the reaction between protons and boron 10 is taken, the energy production comes out too high by a factor of 100,000; if the next heavier element after nitrogen, *i.e.*, oxygen, is assumed to be responsible, the result is too low by a factor of 10,000. For lighter and heavier elements the discrepancy is still greater. Accordingly the carbon cycle is the only nuclear reaction which gives the correct rate of energy production within the limits of uncertainty of the theory.

A great number of stars exists in addition to the sun. Most of these belong to the "main sequence." This sequence extends from the very faint and small "red dwarfs," which are relatively cool, to the very brilliant and massive blue giants whose temperature is very high. The fainter red dwarfs emit about $\frac{1}{100}$ as much light as the sun and have masses about $\frac{1}{4}$ or $\frac{1}{3}$ of the sun's mass. Some of the blue giants, on the other hand, are 10,000 times more luminous than the sun and have a mass from 10 to 20 times the sun's. As the luminosity and the mass increase, the surface temperature of the star increases, and this is responsible for the change of color from red to blue. Together with the surface, the interior also becomes hotter. According to the calculations of Eddington and Strömgren, the sun has a central temperature of about 20,000,000° C., the red dwarfs have perhaps 15,000,000, and at the center of a representative blue giant, Y Cygni (bright), the temperature is about 32,000,000°.

These temperatures, although significantly different from each other, vary only by about a factor of two over the entire main sequence, whereas the luminosity varies by a factor of a million. This phenomenon is so striking that Eddington believed at one time that all main sequence stars had the same temperature at the center. How is this small variation of the central temperature to be explained?

It turns out that this behavior is exactly what should be expected if the stellar energy is produced by nuclear reactions. We have shown in a previous section that the rate of nuclear reactions increases enormously with increasing speed of the reacting nuclei. At any given temperature T, the velocities of the protons are distributed according to the Maxwell-Boltzmann law, and the average velocity is proportional to the square root of T. If these facts are properly taken into account it is found that the rate of energy production varies approximately as the 17th power of the central temperature of the star, at least within the range of temperatures occurring in the main sequence. Therefore Y Cygni, with a central temperature 1.6 times that of the sun, should have an energy production 2,500 times that of the sun. This is in very good agreement with the observed factor of 10,000 if it is remembered that the determination of central temperatures is not very accurate and that other factors, like the density, the total mass of the star, and the concentrations of hydrogen and carbon, also influence the energy production. Similarly good agreement is found for the red dwarfs.

It is evident from this that the energy production in main sequence stars is satisfactorily explained by the theory of the carbon cycle. But there are some stars which do not fall into the main sequence. The most striking ones are the red giants; very brilliant stars of enormous size which, however, have quite low temperatures, both at the surface and in the interior. Their central temperatures range from about 10 to less than 1 million degrees—at least if the accepted theories of stellar structure are correct, and these theories seem to

work very well in the main sequence. At such low temperatures the reactions of the carbon cycle will go exceedingly
slowly, and therefore these stars should be much fainter
than the red dwarfs. In reality, they are as brilliant as the
blue giants. It is entirely unknown at present how the red
giants produce their energy. They may be very young stars
which still have a great amount of lithium or beryllium or
boron in their interior, so that nuclear reactions can occur
at relatively low temperatures. This hypothesis, in fact, has
been made by Gamow and Teller and is probably the most
attractive one proposed so far. But considerable difficulties
are involved in its acceptance.

Similar difficulties are found if one tries to explain the
energy production in the white dwarfs; these are very small
and faint, but very hot, stars. In contrast to the red giants,
it is difficult to understand why so little energy is produced
in the white dwarfs. These difficulties, however, are en-
couraging rather than discouraging. A field of knowledge
begins to become a science when its predictions are definite
enough to lead to contradictions.

THE LIFE OF A STAR

A very natural question is: What is the past and what is
the future of a star? One thing is obvious: The stars must
have a finite age, they cannot have existed for an infinite
time. This is because their energy production uses up the
hydrogen and produces helium; the amount of helium now
in a star sets an upper limit to its age. However, it is likely
that the stars contained some helium when they were
formed. Therefore their actual age cannot be determined
from the present helium content.

We do not know what came before the stars. It is possible that all the material now in single stars was close together in one large mass whose interior was very hot, much
hotter than the stars are today. Under such conditions,

there would be a chance for the building up of the chemical elements from protons. Under present conditions in the interior of stars, only the carbon cycle occurs, only helium is built up from protons, whereas the concentration of all heavier elements remains unchanged.

As shown above, stars live by converting hydrogen into helium. This will cause the mass of the star to decrease somewhat, because a helium atom weighs somewhat less than four hydrogen atoms. However, this decrease of mass is extremely slight; it amounts to only 0.7 per cent even if the entire star consisted originally of hydrogen, and this is completely transformed into helium. This picture is entirely different from the older evolution hypothesis of Russell, which was based on Eddington's hypothesis of energy production by the mutual annihilation of protons and electrons. According to that hypothesis, a star used up its entire mass in producing its radiation, and it was supposed to slide down the main sequence in the course of its evolution, beginning as a giant (blue or red) and ending its life as a red dwarf. None of this remains in our theory: A star always retains about the same mass, barring collisions with another star or other catastrophes which might cause it to split. Since the mass remains constant and observation shows a rather definite relation between mass and brilliance, the star will have approximately the same luminosity, the same surface temperature, and therefore the same color throughout its life.

In fact, the star will change its appearance slightly in the direction opposite to that predicted by the old Eddington-Russell hypothesis. As more and more hydrogen is converted into helium, the star will get hotter, and therefore the carbon cycle will take place at a faster rate. Thus the star, when its fuel supply becomes low, will behave very foolishly and will radiate more energy. Therefore the hydrogen will be consumed faster. Instead of the 30 billion years of prospective life of the sun which we calculated on the basis of its present rate of radiation, there will be "only" 10 or 12 billion years. At the end of this time, the sun will die a brilliant death and will probably transform into a white dwarf, emitting very little radiation. When the last hydrogen is being consumed in the sun, the average temperature of the earth will rise to about 400° C. But there is no reason for us to worry about that—10 billion years, as the *New Yorker* put it, will give ample time to settle our unemployment problems and our wars.

For References see p. 298.

IV

IMAGE FORMATION BY ELECTRONS

By V. K. ZWORYKIN

RCA Research Laboratories
Camden, New Jersey

AN outstanding characteristic of the present century is the rapid widening of the fields of applications of electrons, both in science and in everyday life. Among the newest applications is their use for the formation of images, much as light is used to form optical images. Electron images make possible the electron microscope, with which man can resolve objects at least fifty times smaller than can be seen with the best light microscope; they play a fundamental role in modern television; and find many other interesting and important uses. Indeed the importance of electron imaging has become so great as to give rise to a new branch of electronics known as "electron optics."

An important part of designing an ordinary optical system for forming light images concerns itself with the direct or indirect determination of the paths of light rays through the various lenses. Similarly the determination and control of electron trajectories is the function of electron optics.

Early studies of the behavior of cathode-ray beams under magnetic and electric fields revealed that these rays consisted of particles, later to become known as electrons, which had a fixed ratio of charge to mass, and that the paths could be completely determined by the laws of ordinary mechanics. It soon became evident not only that these cathode rays could be investigated by means of magnetic and electric fields, but also that the converse was true, and that cathode-ray beams could be used to measure these fields. Thus, the first cathode-ray oscillograph, or Braun's tube, came into being. With this tube, the magnitude of rapidly varying voltages applied across one pair of deflecting plates could be observed, if a linearly varying deflecting voltage was applied to the other pair. The cathode-ray beam in these tubes was generated by a low-pressure gas discharge, and the ionized gas molecules in the tube kept the

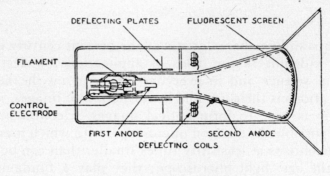

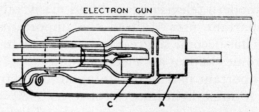

FIG. 16. Early cathode-ray tube, forerunner of the modern oscilloscope tube.

beam concentrated into a narrow bundle. A fluorescent screen on the end of the tube showed the position of the beam as a luminous spot.

A limitation to these tubes soon became apparent. As the rapidity of the variations in the voltage to be measured became greater, making necessary a higher deflection frequency for their observation, it was found that the gas ions which heretofore kept the beam in focus could no longer follow the rapid lateral motion of the beam, and the beam became diffuse.

This difficulty, together with other lesser objections to the Braun tube, led to the development of a tube in which the source of electrons for the cathode-ray beam was a thermionic cathode, and coaxial cylinders or apertures were used to concentrate the beam. Instead of apertures and cylinders, it was also found that electromagnetic coils with their axes parallel to the beam could be equally well used for focusing. A tube of this type, as illustrated in Figure 16, is the forerunner of the modern cathode-ray oscilloscope tube, as well as the Kinescope, or television receiving tube.

While investigating these tubes, an interesting observation was made. It was found that by suitably adjusting the voltages on the concentrating electrodes or on the magnetic focusing coils a clear, enlarged image of the thermionic cathode could be observed on the fluorescent viewing screen. These images, in fact, were frequently used to determine whether the activation of the cathode was uniform, and served as a convenient way of studying defects in the cathode. This tube can be called a forerunner of the electron microscope.

Toward the close of the nineteen-twenties the importance of electron imaging was beginning to be more apparent, and a good deal of theoretical work was being done to determine the nature of this phenomenon. In 1926 a paper was published by H. Busch, in which he showed that there was a complete mathematical analogy between electron trajectories in a potential field and light rays in refractive media; furthermore, he showed that any cylindrically symmetrical electric or magnetic field was capable of forming a first order or Gaussian image. This paper was followed shortly by other theoretical and experimental studies by Picht, Davisson, Knoll, and others, which showed not only the possibility but also the general practicality of electron lenses. By 1932 an electron optics, based upon the analogy between light and electron motion, had become a clearly recognized field.

Once the foundations of this field had been established, progress was rapid, and practical applications followed almost immediately. The systematized knowledge of electron optics could be applied directly to the problem of building an electron gun which was capable of producing the high-density, fine cathode-ray beam required in modern television and cathode-ray tubes. The study of electron paths was applied to the problem of amplifier tubes, and led to the development of the beam power tube, the secondary emission multiplier, and other similar devices. At the same time, much work was done on extended electron images. It was found, for example, that sharp, undistorted, electron images could be reproduced from optical images focused on a photoelectric cathode. Another important application of electron imaging was in the electron microscope. The first compound microscope employing electrons as the imaging means was reported by Knoll and Ruska in 1932. The development of the electron microscope has progressed rapidly and today it has become a practical research tool, capable of resolving objects at least 50 times smaller than can be seen with the best optical instrument. Before giving a more detailed discussion of the principles of construction and application of the electron microscope, I would like to give a brief outline of the elements of electron optics and the principles underlying electron image formation.

Broadly speaking, electron optics is the study of electron paths in electric or magnetic fields. In the design of any electron-optical system, the aim is to determine the shape of the electrodes or magnetic coils which will cause electrons leaving a given point or group of points to reach certain other predetermined points. The problem stated thus has no general solution. Indeed, in all but the simplest cases, it cannot be solved at all. Instead it is necessary to invert the problem and ask what electron trajectories are obtained from a given configuration of electrodes or coils. A system-

atic series of solutions of the latter can be used to answer
the former.

The problem of determining electron trajectories from a
given electrode system at known potentials can be divided
into two parts. First, the potential distribution must be
found from the form of the electrodes. Then the electron
paths can be determined as the electrons move in this field.
Similarly, when magnetic elements are involved, the field
distribution produced by the coils, pole pieces, etc., must
be calculated, and then the electron motion in these fields
sought.

In any charge-free region, the electrostatic potential must
be a solution of the Laplace differential equation, which in
ordinary Cartesian coördinates has the form:

$$\frac{\partial^2\phi}{\partial x^2}+\frac{\partial^2\phi}{\partial y^2}+\frac{\partial^2\psi}{\partial z^2}=0$$

Furthermore, the solution is subject to boundary conditions
such as to make the electrodes equipotential surfaces.

Ordinarily the electron-optical systems encountered in
practice do not require the solution of the general three-
dimensional equation, because most practical systems have
a rather high degree of symmetry. The two most common
types of systems are those which may be termed two-
dimensional, and those involving cylindrical symmetry.
The Laplace equation for these two cases becomes:

$$\frac{\partial^2\phi}{\partial x^2}+\frac{\partial^2\phi}{\partial y^2}=0 \text{ two-dimensional}$$

$$\frac{\partial^2\phi}{\partial z^2}+\frac{1}{r}\frac{\partial}{\partial r}r\frac{\partial\phi}{\partial r}=0 \text{ cylindrical symmetry}$$

Even with these simplifications a mathematical solution of

the equation is very difficult and frequently can only be obtained through the application of approximate methods.

Fortunately, there is a relatively simple experimental method of measuring the potential distribution in an electrode system. The method consists of immersing an enlarged model of the electrode system in an electrolytic bath, applying potentials which are proportional to the working potentials to the various members of the system, and by means of an exploring probe determining the potential distribution of the electrolyte. A space current j flows between the electrodes, which, because no charges accumulate, obeys the equation of continuity

$$\text{div } j = 0$$

Since the conduction in the electrolyte is ohmic, the field strength E is proportional to the current density, hence

$$\text{div } E = 0$$

Therefore, as $E = - \text{grad } \phi$, where ϕ is the potential, the potential distribution within the electrode system immersed in the electrolyte satisfies the Laplace equation and corresponds to the distribution in the actual electrode system.

The typical electrolytic tank used for such measurements is metal lined for purposes of shielding, and is filled with a weak electrolyte—in fact ordinary tap water usually has enough dissolved salts (Fig. 17). The exploring probe is carried on a pantograph which reproduces its motion at a marking stylus over the mapping board. The probe itself is a fine wire point held so that it just breaks the surface of the liquid, this being adequate for any electrode system having mirror symmetry which, as has already been pointed out, includes nearly all those which are of practical importance. When this symmetry is present it is only necessary to make a model of one of the two symmetrical halves of the electrode system. The model is inserted in the tank in such a way that the plane of symmetry coincides with the surface of the liquid. The desired distribution on the plane of symmetry is measured by the probe.

The probe is connected to a carefully calibrated potentiometer through a sensitive current detector which gives a null-indication when the potential of the probe equals that of the electrolyte. Potentiometers are also provided to sup-

FIG. 17. Electrolytic tank for measuring potential distribution in an electrode system.

ply the voltages to the electrodes. In order to avoid polarization effects at the electrodes, 400-cycle a.c. is used instead of direct current. Figure 18 shows a schematic diagram of the plotting tank.

After the potential distribution has been found, either as a result of analysis or from electrolytic measurements, the next step is to determine electron trajectories. Here again, the mathematical difficulties become very great.

Even when the function describing the potential is known, an exact solution of the paths is rarely possible, and approximate or graphical methods must be employed.

From a purely logical standpoint, the electron paths in a potential field could be determined from the Newtonian laws of mechanics in their ordinary form; however, it is

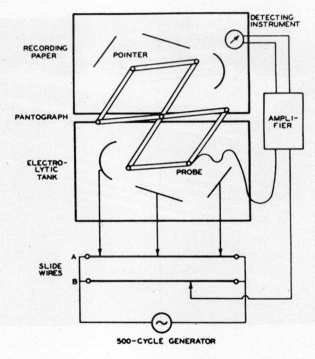

Fig. 18. Diagram of the plotting tank illustrated in Figure 17.

generally more convenient to make use of them expressed as the principle of least action. Where electrostatic fields only are present, the path is defined by the following variational integral.

$$\delta \int_a^b pds = 0$$

where ds is an element of path length, and p is the momentum of the particle, and is given by

$$p = \sqrt{2m\,e\phi}$$

ϕ being the potential at points along the path. Eliminating the constant factor, the integral becomes

$$\delta \int_a^b \sqrt{\phi}\ ds = 0$$

This integral shows clearly the mathematical analogy between electron paths and light rays, because it is identical in form with Fermat's theorem defining the path of a ray of light:

$$\delta \int_a^b nds = 0$$

where n is the index of refraction of the medium along the ray. It will be seen that the square root of the potential plays exactly the same role in an electron-optical system as does the index of refraction in an ordinary optical system. Where magnetic fields are present, the equivalent of an index of refraction for an electronic system can be found, but in this case it is somewhat more complicated, the index being nonisotropic.

One of the simplest methods of plotting electron trajectories, which is applicable to any system having mirror symmetry, is the graphical procedure usually termed the circle method. This method is based on the fact that the centripetal acceleration of an electron moving in a circular path must be balanced by a radial force, that is, a radial field component. Referring to Figure 19 showing the map of a section of the potential field within an electrode system, assume now that an electron is moving through this field with a velocity as indicated by the vector v_0. This electron is acted on by a force e E where E is the field strength at the point it occupies. The force may be resolved into two

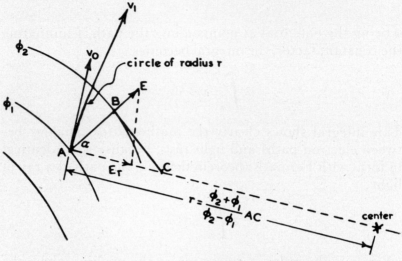

Fɪɢ. 19. Circle method of graphical-ray tracing.

components, one parallel to its direction of motion, the other e E_r at right angles to it. The normal component causes the electron to move in a circular path such that

$$\frac{v_o{}^2}{r} = \frac{eE_r}{m}$$

and since

$$v_o = \sqrt{\frac{2e\phi}{m}}$$

it follows that

$$r = \frac{2\phi}{E_r}$$

Referring again to the figure, it is evident that

$$E_r = E \cos a = \frac{\phi_2 - \phi_1}{A\,B} \cos a = \frac{\phi_2 - \phi_1}{A\,C}$$

and consequently $\quad r = 2\,\dfrac{\phi_1}{\phi_2 - \phi_1}\,A\,C$

or, for greater accuracy

$$r = \frac{\phi_2 + \phi_1}{\phi_2 - \phi_1}\,A\,C$$

The electron trajectory can, therefore, be approximated by a series of circular arcs between the successive equipotentials, the radii and centers of the arcs being obtained by a simple graphical construction indicated in Figure 19 based upon the relation just derived.

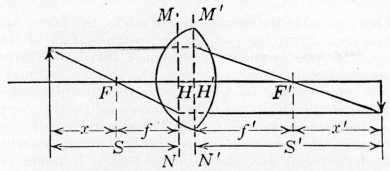

Fig. 20. Illustrating the cardinal points of a thick lens.

Determining the trajectories through electron lenses and the performance of such lenses is a special case of the general problem of electron path determination. As has already been pointed out, the electrodes serving as lenses are cylindrically symmetric, so that the electrolytic tank can be used to determine the potential distribution within them. The circle method can also be used to determine the electron paths through lenses; however, usually the care necessary to obtain the required accuracy does not warrant its application in view of other methods which take advantage of the high degree of symmetry.

The potential field where radial symmetry exists can be expressed as an expansion in terms of the potential distribution on the axis. With this expansion and the Euler form of the principle of least action, a differential equation can be set up which gives the electron path in terms of the axial distribution and its derivatives. This equation, which is termed the ray equation, has the following form:

$$\frac{d^2r}{dz^2} = -\frac{r}{4\phi}\frac{d^2\phi}{dz^2}\left[1 + r^2\left\{\frac{1}{4\phi}\frac{d^2\phi}{dz^2} - \left(\frac{1}{8}\frac{d^4\phi}{dz^4}\Big/\frac{d^2\phi}{dz^2}\right)\right\} + \left(\frac{dr}{dz}\right)^2 + \cdots\right]$$
$$-\frac{1}{2\phi}\frac{dr}{dz}\frac{d\phi}{dz}\left[1 + r^2\left\{\frac{1}{4\phi}\frac{d^2\phi}{dz^2} - \left(\frac{1}{4}\frac{d^3\phi}{dz^3}\Big/\frac{d\phi}{dz}\right)\right\} + \left(\frac{dr}{dz}\right)^2 + \cdots\right]$$

When discussing the performance of a lens, two points are of interest. First, the position and magnification of the image. Second, the quality of the image, that is, its sharpness and freedom from distortion. The position and magnification of the lens are determined by its first-order image properties, namely, its behavior for rays which make a very small angle with the optical axis. These characteristics are generally defined in terms of four cardinal points, namely, two focal points and two principal points. It might be pointed out that for an ordinary thin lens, the two principal points coincide at the lens, and thus the simple relation

$$\frac{1}{u} + \frac{1}{v} = \frac{1}{f}$$

between object distance u, image distance v, and the focal length f is obtained. Similarly, the magnification is given by

$$m = \frac{v}{u}$$

These concepts apply quite generally and, therefore, can be used to define the properties of electron lenses as well as

optical lenses. Thus the problem of finding the first-order
properties of an electron lens involves locating the four cardinal points. Figure 21 illustrates the cardinal points of a
typical thick lens.

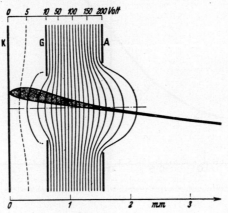

Fig. 21. Illustrating typical ray paths through a lens consisting of two apertures.

In making this determination, since only paraxial trajectories are involved, the ray equation reduces to

$$\frac{d^2r}{dz^2}+\frac{1}{2\phi}\frac{dr}{dz}\frac{\partial\phi}{\partial z}+\frac{1}{4\phi}\frac{\partial^2\phi}{\partial z^2}r=0$$

With the aid of this equation, two rays are traced through
the lens, for example, one parallel to the axis on the image
side, the other parallel to the axis on the object side, as
shown in Figure 20, and from these paths the cardinal
points can be located. The typical ray paths through a lens
consisting of two apertures are illustrated in Figure 21.

In tracing electron rays through such systems, we are
again faced with solving a rather difficult differential equation. In this brief discussion, space does not permit going
into the various methods and short cuts that are helpful in
carrying out the solution of specific problems. There is,

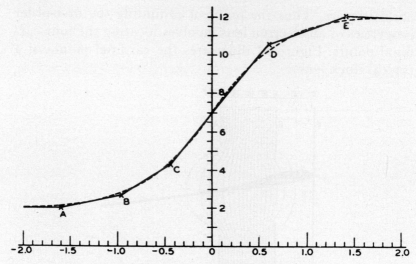

FIG. 22. Illustrating axial potential within an electrode system.

however, one graphical procedure developed by Richard Gans, which I should like to discuss. Figure 22 shows the axial potential within an electrode system consisting of two coaxial equidiameter cylinders. A series of straight lines are substituted for the curve representing the true axial potential distribution, the number depending upon the accuracy required.

Consider now the ray equation; over any straight-line segment the second derivative is zero. Hence, the ray equa-

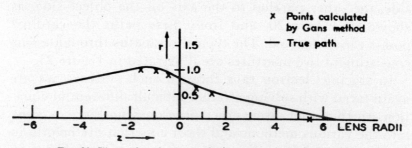

FIG. 23. Illustrating electron paths in system shown in Fig. 22.

tion becomes a simple differential equation which can be
directly integrated twice to give

$$r = r_0 + \frac{2C\,(\sqrt{\phi} - \sqrt{\phi_0})}{S}$$

where $C = \dfrac{dr}{dz}\sqrt{\phi},\; S = \dfrac{d\phi}{dz},$ the slope of the segment,

and r_0, ϕ_0 are the radial position and potential at the beginning of the segment.

At the point where two segments join, there is a singu-

larity, and $\dfrac{d^2\phi}{dz^2}$ is infinite. The ray equation can be inte-

grated over the transition giving

$$\left(\frac{dr}{dz}\right)_2 - \left(\frac{dr}{dz}\right)_1 = -r\,\frac{S_2 - S_1}{4\phi}$$

Here subscripts 1 and 2 indicate values before and after the
break point, respectively. Finally, where the segment is
parallel to the axis, the solution becomes

$$r = r_0 + \left(\frac{dr}{dz}\right)_0 (z - z_0)$$

These three solutions are applied successively to the segments and break points, thus tracing the ray through the
system. Figure 23 shows a path in the system whose axial
potential was given in the previous figure.

So far we have dealt almost exclusively with the problem
of electrostatic lenses. This is because the analytical treatment of electrostatic systems is much simpler than that for
the magnetic systems. For certain simple coil configura-
tions, the magnetic field distribution may be determined

analytically. Many of the coils used in practice, however, are sheathed in iron. The presence of iron greatly complicates the problem. If the iron enclosing the coil has a high permeability, and is operated well below the saturation point, the two poles may be considered as equipotentials of

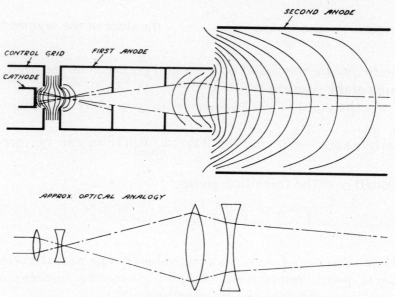

FIG. 24. Illustrating an electron gun and its light-optical analog.

a scalar potential whose gradient is the magnetic field. Under these conditions, the potential distribution, and hence the field, may be determined with the aid of the electrolytic plotting tank. Where these methods cannot be applied, the magnetic distribution must be determined experimentally by means of exploring coils, by the change of resistance of such metals as bismuth, or by the Hall effect.

The first-order ray equation for a magnetic lens has the following form

$$\frac{\partial^2 r}{\partial z^2} = -\frac{eH^2}{8\,m\phi}\,r$$

The radius vector r does not remain in a plane as it does for the electrostatic case but rather rotates about the axis. Therefore, it has the form

$$re^{i\theta} = x + iy$$

The angle θ is given by the integral

$$\theta = \left(\frac{e}{8m}\right)^{\frac{1}{2}} \int_{z_0}^{z} \frac{H}{\sqrt{\phi}} dz$$

Before leaving the discussion of the first-order properties of electron lenses, it should be mentioned that for thin electric and magnetic lenses, that is, those for which the region of varying electrical potential or of magnetic field is small compared with the focal lengths, the principal points may be considered as coinciding at the lens, analogous to the thin optical lens, and the focal lengths will be given by the following integrals:

Electrostatic
$$\frac{1}{f_i} = \frac{3}{16}\left\{\frac{\phi_i}{\phi_o}\right\}^{\frac{1}{4}} \int_{-\infty}^{\infty} \left\{\frac{1}{\phi}\frac{d\phi}{dz}\right\}^2 dz$$

$$\frac{f_i}{f_o} = \left\{\frac{\phi_i}{\phi_o}\right\}^{\frac{1}{2}}$$

(i denotes image side of lens)

Magnetic
$$\frac{1}{f} = \frac{e}{8m\phi} \int_{-\infty}^{\infty} H^2\, dz$$

The discussion given above has been restricted to the first-order properties of electron lenses. From a practical standpoint, the perfection of the electron image is of equal or

greater importance. The lens defects of electronic systems
are quite analogous to those in light lenses. Considerations
of the behavior of paraxial rays, with one exception, reveal
nothing of the image defects of a given lens. In order to determine the aberrations, it is necessary to consider rays
which make an appreciable angle with the axis of the system. Although it was not explicitly mentioned, first-order
imaging, which gives the cardinal points, assumes that the
trigonometric function describing the passage of the rays
from the object point, through the lens, and to the image
point, is expanded in a power series of r and that terms involving all but first powers of r can be neglected. The Seidel
theory of aberrations includes the terms involving the third
power of r. Second power terms vanish because of symmetry
requirements. There are five aberrations on the basis of this
theory. These are:

> Spherical aberration
> Astigmatism
> Coma
> Curvature of the image field
> Distortion

In addition, there is another image defect due to variations in the velocity of electrons. This defect is analogous
to chromatic aberration in light systems, and is given the
same name.

Let us examine these aberrations briefly.

Spherical aberration is due to rays passing through the
outer parts of a lens, which do not converge on the paraxial
image point. This aberration differs from the other four
third-order aberrations in that it affects points on the axis
of the system.

Astigmatism occurs when rays from an object point,
lying in a plane including the axis of this system, converge
on a point which is different from that upon which rays
lying in a plane normal to the axis converge.

Coma is the result of rays through different parts of the lens not meeting in a common image point, but differs from spherical aberration in that it vanishes for object points on the axis. Its name is derived from the comet-shaped area over which rays from an object point meet the image plane.

Curvature of the image field, as the name implies, means that image points from a plane object do not lie in a plane.

Distortion of the image is due to a nonuniformity of magnification or to a twist of the image.

The procedure for calculating these aberrations in an actual system is extremely difficult and laborious, and is beyond the scope of this discussion.

Most of these defects can be reduced and some practically eliminated by a proper design of the electron-optical system. Instead of attempting to describe general methods of dealing with these various aberrations, let us consider some of the practical applications of these lenses and discuss the aberrations as related to specific problems.

APPLICATIONS OF ELECTRON OPTICS

The utility of a cathode-ray tube, whether for use as an oscilloscope or for television purposes, depends, as has already been pointed out, upon the ability to produce an extremely fine electron beam, having a relatively high current density. For this an electron-optical system which is roughly analogous to an optical projection spotlight is required. The system which serves this function is usually termed the electron gun. Guns used in modern tubes are almost universally made up with two lens elements. The first lens, that is, the lens nearest the cathode, is usually electrostatic, whereas the second lens may be either electrostatic or magnetic. The cathode is located at one extremity and is usually an indirectly heated oxide-coated emitter. Immediately adjacent to the cathode is the first lens system, consisting of two apertured discs, one of which is the control grid governing the current in the beam, the other the first anode. This lens causes the electrons leaving the cathode to converge into a narrow bundle, called the cross-over. The cross-over is the point where the principal rays from the emitter meet the axis, and corresponds to the exit pupil of the analogous optical system.

The second lens generally used in the gun is also electro-static, and is made up of the first and second anode cylinders. The potentials of these cylinders are so adjusted that the cross-over is imaged on the fluorescent screen, mosaic, or any other element of the tube, where the small spot is required.

It may seem surprising at first sight that a reduced image of the cathode is not formed on the screen but instead an image of the cross-over. However, it turns out that for a given spot size and lens the maximum current density can be obtained by imaging the cross-over.

Since the second lens essentially focuses an image point on the axis into an object point, the only third-order lens defect which needs be considered is spherical aberration. This aberration acts, of course, to increase the spot size. By properly shaping the electrodes in an electrostatic gun, or the lens coil of a magnetic gun, it is possible to reduce this aberration. However, even with these corrections, it is necessary to place a limiting aperture near the second lens to mask off the outer part of the lens.

Two lens defects at the first lens make the cross-over larger than would be predicted from the first-order theory. These are due to variations of initial velocities and to space charge effects. The former is related to the velocities of emission from the thermionic cathode. The second is due to the mutual repulsion between electrons where the charge density is high. These defects place a limit on the current density and fineness of the cross-over.

The details of the construction of an electron gun depend,

of course, upon the applications for which it is intended. A gun to be used in an Iconoscope for television pickup must be capable of producing a minute spot of only a few thousandths of an inch in its greatest dimension. However, the beam current is small—of the order of a tenth of a microampere or less. Furthermore, the sensitivity and shape of the control grid characteristic are unimportant. The gun is located in the long glass neck. Opposite the gun is the mosaic—the photosensitive element which plays the fundamental role in converting a light image into a picture signal. A normal Iconoscope is shown in Figure 25.

FIG. 25. Normal Iconoscope.

The gun used in the Kinescope, or viewing tube, is the same in principle as that in the Iconoscope. The requirements are, however, quite different. The current needed is much greater, being of the order of a milliampere. Against this the permissible spot diameter is larger. Since the picture is reproduced by varying the beam current as the spot sweeps across the fluorescent screen, the control characteristic of the grid is a matter of utmost importance.

Television projection Kinescopes, tubes reproducing pictures in sufficient brightness so that the image can be thrown on a large screen, employ guns which require perhaps the greatest engineering skill in their design. These guns must not only produce an extremely small spot, but must also be capable of delivering even more current than those of the ordinary Kinescope. In order to obtain the necessary brightness, the projection Kinescope is operated at very high voltages, that is, 50 to 70 kv. Although this introduces insulation, corona, and cold discharge problems, it makes the electron-optical design somewhat simpler.

Another application of electron optics, which I would like to describe, represents a rather different type of imaging than occurs in the electron gun. This is the electron imaging system developed to increase the sensitivity of the Iconoscope. The scene to be televised is focused on a large semitransparent photocathode. Electrons which leave the photosensitive surface are distributed according to the intensity variations of the light image. An electron lens system refocuses these electrons into an electron image of the original scene. By allowing the electron image to fall on a mosaic which has a high secondary-emission ratio so that for every photoelectron which strikes it several electrons leave, the sensitivity of the pickup tube can be increased.

The electron lens employed in this imaging device is based upon the potential distribution between two coaxial,

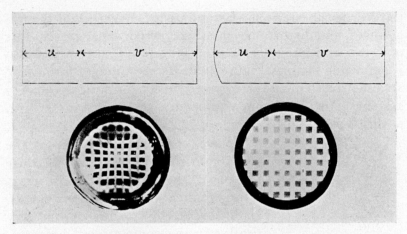

FIG. 26. Illustrating images formed by a corrected (*right*) and an uncorrected (*left*) electron optical imaging system.

equidiameter cylinders. However, in order to overcome aberrations which would otherwise make the system un-usable, it is necessary to modify the simple basic arrange-ment. Since the electron-ray bundles passing through the lens are small, spherical aberration is negligible. Likewise coma, although present to a somewhat greater extent, is not great enough to constitute a limiting factor. The three

FIG. 27. Iconoscope equipped with corrected imaging system.

third-order aberrations—astigmatism, curvature of the image field, and distortion—if not corrected, cause serious loss of detail and image perfection. Chromatic aberration also is a limiting factor. Figure 26 illustrates images formed by an uncorrectted and a corrected electron-optical imaging system. An Iconoscope equipped with an imaging system of this type is shown in Figure 27.

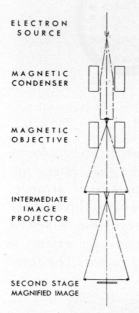

ELECTRON
SOURCE

MAGNETIC
CONDENSER

MAGNETIC
OBJECTIVE

INTERMEDIATE
IMAGE
PROJECTOR

SECOND STAGE
MAGNIFIED IMAGE

FIG. 28. A schematic representation of the elements in the electron microscope.

I have reserved discussion of the electron microscope until last, because it is one of the newest and most interesting applications of electron optics. In principle this microscope is very similar to the conventional light microscope. Figure 28 shows schematically the fundamental elements making up the electronic instrument. Each microscope has a source of the radiation used for making observations, condenser lenses for concentrating the radiation onto the specimen, an objective lens which forms an enlarged first image of the specimen, and a projection lens which forms the final image. In the electron microscope the source of radiation is a thermionic cathode. Electrons from the source are accelerated to a high velocity as soon as they have left the cathode. The electron lens used in the electron microscope may be either electrostatic or magnetic, and comparable results have been obtained with both types of systems. However, so far most electron microscopes in use at present are equipped with magnetic lenses, chiefly because of certain practical considerations.

Let us consider first the imaging process by which the

enlarged first image is obtained. An analysis of the physics of image formation either with light or electrons shows that it is closely related to the phenomenon of diffraction, and consequently dependent upon the size of the object being imaged, the angular aperture *a* of the lens, and the wave length λ of the radiation employed. The expression which

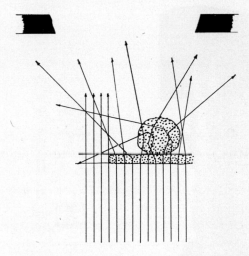

Fig. 29. Electron scattering in the electron microscope.

gives the size of the smallest detail which can be resolved is the following:

$$d = \frac{0.5\lambda}{\mu \sin a}$$

Since for visible light the smallest wave length that can be used is in the neighborhood of 4,000 Å, and the maximum index of refraction of the fluid immersing the object is 1.7, even if sin *a* is given its maximum value of unity, the smallest distinguishable distance is about 1,200 Å. (P. 226.)

Where high-velocity electrons are used as the observing medium, the minimum distinguishable distance is very much smaller. The effective wave length of electrons in motion is given by

$$\lambda = \sqrt{\frac{150}{V}} \quad \text{Angstrom Units}$$

FIG. 30. RCA electron microscope.

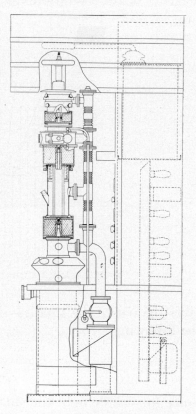

FIG. 31. Structural plan of the RCA electron microscope shown in Figure 30.

where V is the electron velocity in volts, a relation which is derived from the wave mechanics of matter. Electron velocities of 60 kv. or more are used in practical electron microscopes, and hence the effective wave lengths are less than .05 Å or $\frac{1}{100,000}$ that of light. The angular aperture at the object is determined by the spherical aberration of the lens and, as will be explained later, the method of imaging. For objectives such as are used in present-day electron microscopes, the aperture is of the order of one or two thousandths. Hence objects as small as 10 or 20 Å can theoretically be resolved. This is in close agreement with the observed performance of the modern electron microscope.

Fig. 32. Illustrating air lock of electron microscope as described on page 101.

It was mentioned that the size of the objective aperture is related to the method of forming the image. In the conventional light microscope light passing through the specimen is absorbed in varying amounts at different points, and it is this variation in transmission that produces the differences in intensity of light in the final image. The specimens used in an electron microscope are usually completely trans-

parent so that all the electrons striking the object are transmitted through it. However, although electrons are not absorbed by the specimen, they are scattered, the amount of
scattering at each point being a function of the density and
thickness of the object (Fig. 29). Electrons which are scat-

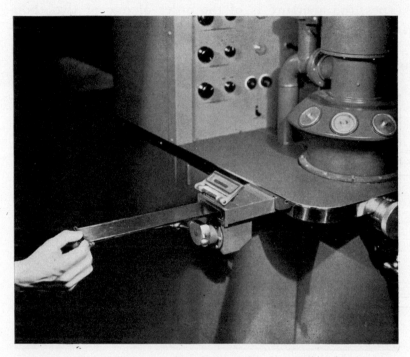

FIG. 33. Air lock of electron microscope for photographic plates.

tered through more than a certain predetermined angle are
intercepted by the limiting aperture, so that the electron
density in the image will vary with the thickness and density. It will be evident from this that the contrast depends
upon the size of the limiting aperture and that, leaving aside
all considerations of spherical aberration in the objective
lens, a small aperture must be used if high contrast is to be
obtained.

The electron projection lens, which forms the final image from the intermediate image, does not limit the attainable resolving power. The angular aperture of the electron-ray bundles entering the projection lens is so small that spherical aberration effects in this element are entirely negligible.

The construction of the new RCA electron microscope is shown in Figures 30 and 31.

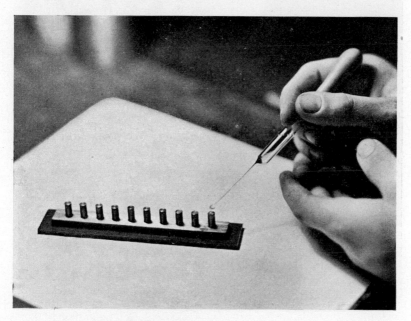

FIG. 34. Mounting objects for examination in electron microscope.

The complete microscope stands about 7 feet high, occupies not more than 5 square feet of floor space, and is completely shielded from electrical and magnetic disturbances. Thus it can be fitted into any research laboratory, and does not require a special shielded room to house it, as did the earlier instruments (Fig. 30).

The cathode and gun are located at the very top of the

instrument. Below them are the condenser lens, the objective, and the projection lens. The specimen is held in the object chamber, which will be described in some detail a

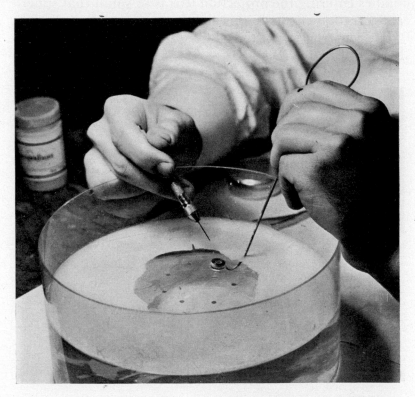

Fig. 35. Formation of cellulose film.

little later. Finally, there is a fluorescent screen, pivoted in such a way that it can be moved into position to receive the electron image or rotated back so that photographic plates placed below it are exposed. The entire electron-optical path is maintained at a pressure of about 10^{-5} mm Hg by an oil diffusion pump.

The power supplies for the over-all microscope voltage

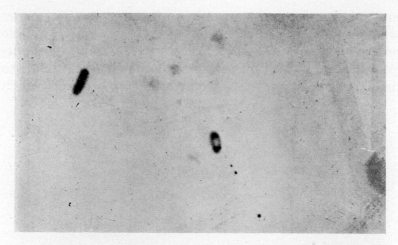

FIG. 36. Photomicrograph of the hay bacillus (*Bacillus subtilis*) taken with ordinary microscope, × 2,500. Cf. Figure 37.

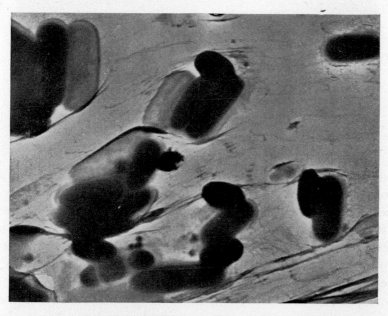

FIG. 37. Electron micrograph of *Bacillus subtilis*, × 12,500.

and for the electron-lens coils are located in the cabinet which forms the rear portion of the instrument. These power supplies require very careful design, since the slightest variation in over-all voltage or in lens current tends to defocus the instrument. Special circuits are provided which

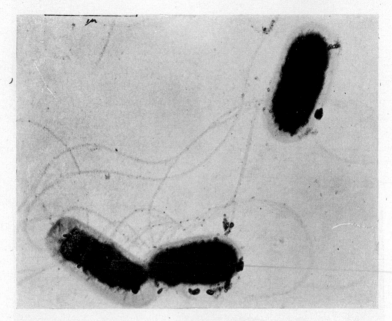

FIG. 38. Electron micrograph of *Aerobacter cloacae*, × 24,000

hold the high voltage and the objective lens current to a constancy of one part in 50,000. The condenser and projection lenses do not require quite as careful regulation, and are made constant to 0.02 per cent and 0.004 per cent, respectively. With this degree of stability, the electrical circuits impose no limitation on the resolving power even below 10 Å.

As has already been pointed out, the main body of the microscope is maintained at a high vacuum. Since the volume of the main chamber of the present microscope is rather large, if it were necessary to let air into the instrument each time a specimen is changed, considerable delay would be encountered. To avoid this, an air lock is provided

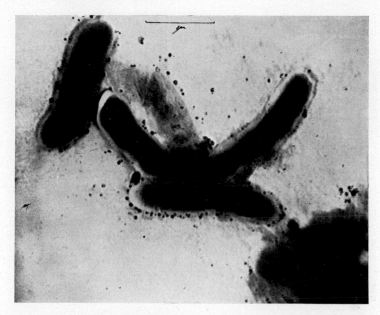

Fig. 39. Electron micrograph of organism (*Mycobacterium tuberculosis, typus humanus*) producing tuberculosis, × 18,000.

at the object chamber, arranged so that the specimen can be moved into a small chamber which can be sealed off from the rest of the instrument. To remove the specimen, therefore, it is only necessary to let air into this small compartment. The new object is then placed in the chamber, the chamber evacuated, and the object moved into its place above the objective. The whole operation of changing a specimen requires only 60 seconds. While discussing the object chamber, mention should be made of the fact that delicate controls are provided to give transverse motion of the object in two directions, thus permitting the observer to view any portion of the specimen he desires. The air lock and object are illustrated in Figure 32.

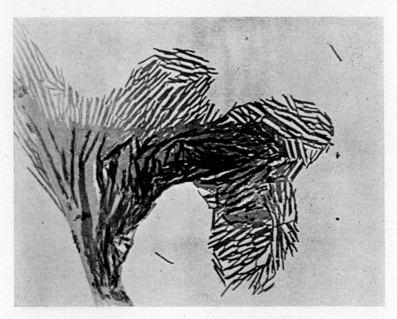

FIG. 40. Electron micrograph of a filterable virus (tobacco mosaic), × 21,000.

During operation it is, of course, necessary to change photographic plates. Therefore, an air lock is also provided for the photographic chamber. The photographic plates used with the microscope are long enough so that a number of exposures may be made on the same plate, and an adjustable mask allows the width of the picture to be controlled at will (Fig. 33).

The specimens for the electron microscope must be mounted quite differently from those for an ordinary microscope, since the electrons will not penetrate an ordinary glass slide. The most frequent procedure used for mounting objects for examination is to suspend them in pure water or other suitable liquid, then to place a drop of the sus-

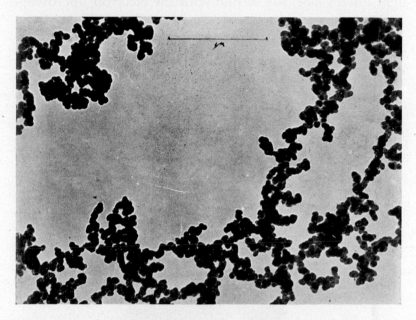

Fig. 41. Electron micrograph of a chemical preparation with particles too small to be resolved with light × 26,000.

pension on an extremely thin cellulose film which is supported on a fine mesh screen (Fig. 34). The supporting film, which is of the order of 100 Å thick, is made by spreading a droplet of a solution of the celluloid on water. The formation of such a film is illustrated in Figure 35. Other procedures are to suspend the object particles on the cellulose itself, or, where the object is self-supporting, to mount the specimen directly on the wire mesh.

The performance can best be described by showing micrographs that have been made with the instrument. In the fields of biology and bacteriology, the new microscope is a tool of immense importance. Figures 36 and 37 are micrographs of *Bacillus subtilis;* the first was made with a good light microscope, the second with the electron microscope.

FIG. 42. Electron micrograph of a substance with particles too small to be revealed by light optics, × 23,000.

The former shows a resolving power of about 2,000 Å, while objects of less than 100 Å in size can be resolved on the latter. In Figure 38 are some specimens of *Aerobacter cloacae,* showing the flagella by which the organisms attain mobility. Figure 39 illustrates the organism responsible for human tuberculosis. Filterable viruses, which have heretofore been unobservable because they are beyond the range of the optical microscope, can be easily resolved with the

FIG. 43. Electron micrograph of vinyl chloride, polymerized, × 41,000.

FIG. 44. Electron micrograph of vinyl chloride, slightly polymerized, × 18,500.

electron microscope. Tobacco mosaic virus is illustrated in Figure 40.

As great as is the importance of this instrument in biology and bacteriology, its value to research and industrial

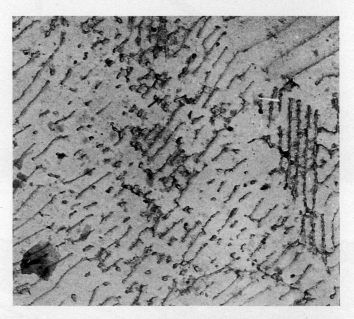

FIG. 45. Electron micrograph of etched steel, × 11,000.

chemistry is fully as great. For instance, details of surface conditions far below the resolving power of a light microscope have a considerable effect on absorption and other chemical properties. Figure 41 illustrates the appearance of a chemical preparation where the size of the particles is too small to be resolved with light. Another commercial chemical product having a platelike character unrevealed with an optical microscope is shown in Figure 42. Figures 43 and 44 illustrate the difference between vinyl chloride which is polymerized, and some which is only slightly polymerized.

The applications of the microscope even extend into the realm of metallurgy, although this is an entirely new field,

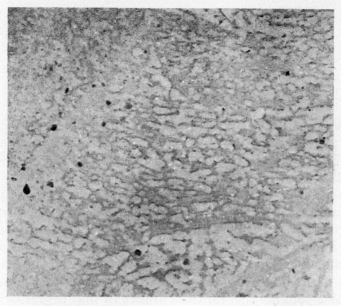

Fig. 46. Electron micrograph of etched steel, × 10,000.

and the technique is not yet fully developed. Two sample electron micrographs of etched steel are shown in Figures 45 and 46.

These micrographs illustrate the wide range of applications to which the instrument can be adapted and also its tremendous resolving power. Some of the pictures show details as fine as 30 Å, in other words, between 50 and 100 times smaller than can be seen with the best optical instrument.

For References see p. 299.

RECENT WORK IN THE FIELD OF HIGH PRESSURES

By P. W. BRIDGMAN

Harvard University

EVER since 1905 I have been engaged in the measurement of various physical effects produced by high pressures. During these years the range of the pressures attainable has been considerably increased, and the scope of the phenomena investigated has become broad enough so that a general survey of the steps in the development of this field is now of interest, both for the new phenomena discovered and for the suggestions which may be afforded as to tactics for the invasion of a new field of physics. From the point of view of tactics it is fortunate that the field of high pressures is not a popular one, for the absence of that degree of competition which characterizes such a subject as nuclear physics, for example, has made it possible for the subject to develop primarily under the stimulus of scientific expediency, without extraneous motives.

HISTORICAL BACKGROUND

The high-pressure field divides naturally into several domains of successively higher pressures, each domain being set off by the sort of phenomena which are most important within it or by the sort of technique necessary to exploit it. The first domain may be taken to be that of critical phenomena in gases; here the characteristic pressures are 200 or 300 atmospheres. The techniques are simple, for it is possible to use heavy glass capillaries to contain the gases under pressure, so that the phenomena can be examined visually, and to make pressure-tight joints with such simple means as sealing wax. This domain was opened with the discovery of critical phenomena by Andrews in the middle of the last century and was extensively cultivated until perhaps 1890. By this time the field was pretty well exhausted, both the critical and other phenomena in it having been explored. Most of these other effects, however, such as that of pressure on the electrical resistance of metals, were so small and difficult to measure that there was no agreement with regard to numerical results, and comparatively few serious measurements were attempted.

The second domain in the high-pressure field reaches roughly to 3,000 kg/cm^2,* which is about the pressure prevailing in modern artillery. The research in this region was most intense from 1890 to 1905; the two outstanding investigators were Amagat [1] and Tammann [2]. Amagat's work was a natural outgrowth of the previous work on critical phenomena. His pressures were far above the critical pressures of ordinary gaseous substances; at the top of the range the ordinary gases become essentially liquid in all important properties, although they do not pass through a condensation point. Amagat's most important work was a measurement of the pressure-volume-temperature relations of a number of liquids or gases through this domain. Tammann's investigations connected liquids on the other side with solids, and he was mostly concerned with determining the effect of pressures in this domain on melting or freezing temperature. The technique of the domain up to pressures of 3,000 kilograms per square centimeter (kg/cm^2) was mostly contributed by Amagat. Among other things he devised a form of packing that was totally enclosed and initially compressed with heavy screws, and that did not begin to leak until the top pressures were reached; it was leak that set the limit of the domain and circumscribed the feasible

* 3,000 kg/cm^2 is equivalent to 42,600 lb/in^2.

manipulations. Amagat also devised an accurate method of measuring pressure, which demanded high precision in machining operations and which probably would not have been possible at a much earlier date.

THE PRESSURE RANGE UP TO 20,000 Kg/cm^2

When my work was started in 1905 it was my intention to study certain optical effects. I had no expectation of reaching pressures anywhere near the limits set by Amagat, since, for one thing, it was necessary to use glass for visibility. After my apparatus was constructed and some preliminary manipulations were made, there was an explosion— something very likely to happen with glass, which is most capricious. This destroyed an essential part of the apparatus, which had to be reordered from Europe; the United States had not at that time acquired its present degree of instrumental independence. In the interval of waiting for the replacement I tried to make other use of my apparatus for generating pressure. While designing a closure for a pressure vessel, so that it could be rapidly assembled or taken apart, I saw that the design hit upon did more than originally intended; the vessel automatically became tighter when pressure was increased, so that there was no reason why it should ever leak. A simple application of the general principle is shown in Figure 47. This at once opened an entirely new pressure field, limited only by the strength of the containing vessels and not by leak. My intended optical experiment was therefore dropped; the laboratory wrote off the expense of the replacement part and of the apparatus already constructed, and the development of the new field was begun. I have never returned to the original problem. This was a case where pertinacity of purpose would not have been good tactics.

The first problem in the new field was to find the limit imposed by the strength of the containing vessel. One would

expect, perhaps, that the requisite information would be
contained in an engineering treatise on the strength of
materials. It soon appeared, however, that little help was
to be found there; the conditions of engineering practice

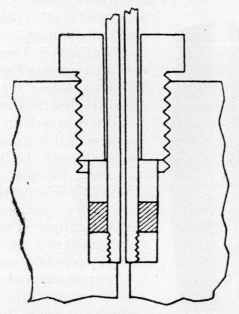

Fɪɢ. 47. The general scheme of the packing by which pressure in the soft packing
material is automatically maintained a fixed percentage higher than in the liquid.

were not sufficiently close to the new conditions. For one
thing the limits imposed by engineering theories have seldom been adequately checked, due to the latitude allowed
by the very liberal factors of safety always employed. In fact,
sometimes the commonly quoted engineering criteria of rupture gave positively incorrect results under the new conditions. It was necessary, therefore, before entering the new
domain, to turn aside and make a systematic investigation
of the strength of the pressure vessels and other essential
parts of any pressure apparatus, such as the pistons. This

investigation was necessarily rather extensive, and included a search for the strongest kinds of steel.

From this investigation new facts and new points of view were obtained with regard to the rupture of ordinary engineering materials [3]. For instance, thick cylinders were found to break on the outside instead of the inside, as was commonly expected. Two such cylinders are shown in Figures 48 and 49. Fortunately the maximum pressures that thick cylinders can withstand proved to be notably in excess of that indicated by the simple theories. In this exploratory work, fractures of the pressure apparatus were common, and under circumstances not without danger. These were finally traced to a new type of rupture, the possibility of which was not commonly recognized and which even now some people find difficult to accept. This is rupture

Fig. 48. Outside view of a ruptured cylinder. The rupture started at the outside surface.

by a separation of fibers, with no corresponding component of stress, there being only an extension, but no tension, in the direction of rupture. This I have called the "pinching-off" effect; a specimen is shown in Figure 50.

The pressures reached in the work of exploration were sometimes as high as 40,000 kg/cm^2, but these were attainable only in a soft solid, like lead, and could not be used to give useful information about other sorts of physical phenomena than rupture itself. It appeared that the pressures at which useful physical measurements could be made were much lower, perhaps less than one-half as much.

For a number of years my experiments were confined to mapping out the important physical phenomena in the

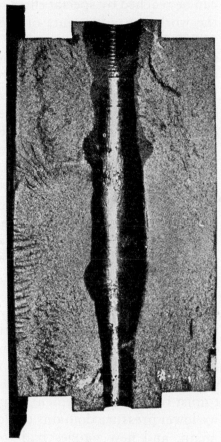

Fig. 49. One of the halves of a cylinder of tool steel split by an internal pressure of 450,000 lbs. per square inch. The internal bore has stretched from 0.50 to 1.20 inches.

domain thus opened. A characteristic of the domain is that the pressures are limited by the strength of containing vessels made as simply as possible, in a single piece, of the best heat-treated alloy steels available. The exact range to which one is confined in this domain is determined by several

tactical considerations. If the phenomenon is of special interest, higher pressures than usual can be reached by special effort. Very early in the work, measurements of pressures up to 21,000 kg/cm² had been made in following the melting curve of water. This was of particular interest at the time, and I considered it worth the effort, but the apparatus survived only a single application of pressure; it received so much permanent stretch as to make it useless for other work. Obviously scientific economy usually demands a less destructive lower limit. The life of the apparatus increases very rapidly as the pressure range is lowered. Most of my work involved a maximum pressure of 12,000 kg/cm²; apparatus with no initial flaw will withstand several hundred applications of pressure in this range without fracture.

FIG. 50. A "pinched-off" specimen as described on p. 112.

The range having been fixed, I had to decide the sort of phenomena to investigate and the order in which to measure them. One of the most important questions of scientific tactics is that of order, as it is, indeed, with other kinds of tactics. Obviously first on the list must be the measurement of pressure. The gauges of the two lower pressure domains could not be used in the new domain, and new gauges had to be devised. Gauges may be divided into primary and secondary; the primary gauges serve to calibrate the secondary ones, which are the working gauges used in the actual measurements. The calibration is much facilitated by the establishment of pressure-fixed points of reference, similar to the fixed temperature points of thermometry. Such pressure-fixed points are given by the pressures of melting or of polymorphic transition of standard substances at specified temperatures, and were established in the new domain.

Accuracy is always a problem that has to be considered. How much time should one spend in preparatory work to ensure that the results are accurate? It is unpleasant to think that all one's work will have to be done over again at some later time, and so there is a temptation to delay for refinement. No absolute basis for decision can exist under the circumstances, for the accuracy should be controlled by the sort of phenomenon that is being investigated, and how can one anticipate the sort of phenomena in a new domain or predict the course that physical theory will take in order to know what will be the significant measurements to refine? The compromise that the investigator adopts will be largely determined by his temperament and his hunch of what is going to be important. In my own case I am afraid that nature was mostly permitted to take its course. A certain degree of accuracy was obtainable without too great effort with the pressure gauges adapted for the new domain, and this I accepted, hoping that it would be sufficient. Up to 12,000 it proved to be possible to measure pressure easily with an accuracy of about 0.1 per cent. In justification of having rested content with 0.1 per cent, it may be said that at that time physical theory did not seem to demand even as accurate a knowledge as this of those phenomena that would be naturally studied at these pressures. The theory of liquids, for example, certainly was not in a position to demand such accuracy.

COMPRESSIBILITY OF LIQUIDS

In the absence of more compelling considerations, the order in which phenomena should be investigated in a new domain is dictated by ease of investigation. Technical difficulties are sure to arise, but success in meeting these difficulties will increase with practice and control of the simpler operations. For this reason the first measurements made were of the compressibility of liquids. The volume changes in liquids are so great, ranging up to 30 per cent, that the measurements are easily made with the requisite accuracy. This constitutes a great advance beyond the first measurements of the compressibility of liquids, when there was difficulty in establishing even the existence of a volume compressibility with sensitive piezometers made in the form of overgrown thermometers.

Another advantage in first measuring the volume compressibility of liquids was that Amagat had also measured it. In addition to the intrinsic interest in extending his results, a comparison of the results obtained from my studies with those of Amagat at the low-pressure end of the range would afford a check of the new methods. Also the compressibility of the liquids entered as an essential factor in the design of the apparatus, whose proportions were determined by the necessity of reaching the maximum pressure in a single stroke of the piston, which, in turn, depended on the compressibility of the liquids with which pressure was transmitted. The measurements on the liquids used by Amagat were made, and checks on the pressure measurements were obtained. As a result, new phenomena in liquids were found that had not been suspected by Amagat, such as the reversal of the behavior of thermal expansion with temperature at high pressures.

After the measurements on these liquids, the next phenomenon, both from the point of view of ease and of interest in the results, was an extension to higher pressures of Tammann's measurements on melting. This study also yielded important new results, for it turned out that the course of the melting curve was not what Tammann had anticipated from an extrapolation of his results. He had expected that the curve would be found to pass through a maximum temperature, if pressure could be extended to the magnitudes of the new domain. This was found not to be the case. Neither did the melting curve end in a critical point between liquid and solid, in analogy with the critical point between liquid and gas, as was expected by a number of theorists; instead it became evident that it would rise indefinitely with pressure and temperature.

POLYMORPHISM UNDER PRESSURE

Closely related, both instrumentally and thermodynamically, to the change of phase of a substance by melting is the change of phase by a polymorphic transition from one solid form to another. The thermodynamics of the transition between solids is governed by the same equation as melting, and the parameters of the transition can be determined by exactly the same instrumental manipulations. A few cases of such polymorphism had been studied by Tammann in the previous pressure range. His most spectacular result was that ordinary ice is transformed by pressures above 2,000 kg/cm^2 into another variety of ice which is denser than the liquid, so that the abnormal behavior of water, which sets it off from other substances in that it expands when freezing, disappears at high pressures. Tammann also found a third variety of ice at lower temperatures than the melting curve. One of my first results in this field was the discovery that there are still other varieties of ice. Tammann's high-pressure ice is stable only a short distance beyond the pressure range he used, being replaced at 3,500 by another form, and this in turn at 6,400 by another. I have found quite recently that still another variety is formed at 22,000. In all, there are seven different kinds of ice with known regions of stability, and the melting point of one of them reaches as high as 175° C. under pressures which I have recently attained.

Polymorphism proved to be a more common phenomenon in the new pressure range than would have been anticipated from its frequency in the lower range, and my investigations have disclosed many examples of it. During the course of work in this field another kind of transition came to light [4]: a transformation of yellow phosphorus to black at pressures of about 12,000 and at temperatures above 200° C. This type of transition is irreversible thermodynamically, and the product is stable at atmospheric pressure. The new black phosphorus differs in important respects from the yellow; for instance, it is a conductor of electricity and is stable in the air. Later, Jacobs [5] made a more elaborate study and found further complexities in the transformation.

The techniques involved in the measurements of the compressibility and of the melting of liquids are closely related, they depend on a determination of the displacement of the piston as a function of pressure, and require therefore a packing absolutely free from leak. From the experience gained by several years of piston-displacement measurements, I felt qualified to embark on the examination of other sorts of phenomena. Again the next step was dictated by considerations of instrumental ease and simplicity. The subject chosen was the measurement of the effect of pressure on the electrical resistance of metals. Measurements in the previous pressure domains had shown unsatisfactory agreement, because of the smallness of the effect. For example, the effect of 1,000 kg/cm² pressure on copper is to decrease the resistance by only 0.2 per cent. But with the larger effects to be expected in the wider pressure range sufficient accuracy would probably not be hard to attain. This turned out to be the case. However, in order to secure the desired accuracy, a temperature control was necessary to about 0.01° C.; approximately the limit that was feasible to attempt. Another feature of technique demanded by the resistance measurements was some method of getting electrically insulated connections, or leads, into the pressure

chamber; this problem, however, had already been sufficiently well solved for these experiments in connection with
the secondary pressure gauge, which utilized the change in
resistance of manganin under pressure.

PRESSURE AND THERMOELECTRIC PROPERTIES

After the measurements of electrical resistance, simple
extensions of technique made it possible to measure the
effect of pressure on thermoelectric properties of metals, and
a number of such measurements were made. The new experimental results on resistance and thermoelectric properties
might naturally be expected to have some significance for the
electron theory of metals, which at that time was showing
renewed life. I spent a good deal of time speculating on the
possible significance of the pressure effects for the mechanism of conduction, and did get a new point of view which
had its elements of interest for a while but was presently
made obsolete by wave mechanics.

A natural suggestion arising from theoretical speculations was that it would be desirable to determine the effect
of pressure on thermal conductivity of metals, since it was
known that there is a simple connection between electrical and thermal conductivity, which is formulated in the
Wiedemann-Franz law. Measurements were made, therefore, of the effect of pressure on the thermal conductivity of
a number of metals, and the results were different from
those anticipated from the simple theory. This proved to be
an occasion, however, when the tactics dictated by the de-
sire to play into the demands of theory proved ill advised,
because the subject was of great experimental difficulty and
the accuracy in the final result was not sufficient. Better
advised tactics would have delayed the investigation of this
effect until the technique of the domain had been more
completely mastered. Later, Starr [6], working in my laboratory, repeated the measurements under better condi-

tions, so that the effects are now sufficiently well established, at least for a few metals. The thermal conductivity of liquids proved to be much easier to measure than that of solids, since the effects are larger and the numerical values more advantageous. A number of such determinations were made for common liquids, which brought to light a simple correlation between thermal conductivity in amorphous substances and mechanical properties that is valid outside the pressure domain [7].

COMPRESSIBILITY OF SOLIDS

Not until all these measurements were completed did I attempt the measurement that, from the point of view of today, one would be tempted to think the simplest of all and most immediately utilizable by theory, namely, that of the compressibility of solids, in particular, metals and simple salts. One reason why this was not done sooner is that it is only comparatively recently that there has been any stimulus from the theoretical side to do it. In the early years of the century it was thought that the order in which matter would be understood theoretically was gases, liquids, and solids. However, with the development of theories of the solid state around 1920, in the hands of Born [8] and others, it became evident that solids, as well as gases, are simple, and that the study of liquids would have to be left until the last. Furthermore, from the point of view of technique, experiments on the compressibility of solids are very much easier to write about than to do. The effects are small and are obscured by the distortions of the pressure apparatus, which are of the same order of magnitude, whereas, when the compressibility of liquids is concerned, the distortion of the apparatus is of a lower order of magnitude. However, there was an advantage in being able to make the attempt in higher pressure domains, where the effects (which are proportional to the pressure) are larger than in lower pressure regions. There was, therefore, more prospect of success. It turned out that the problem was now capable of satisfactory solution; methods were found for eliminating the dis-

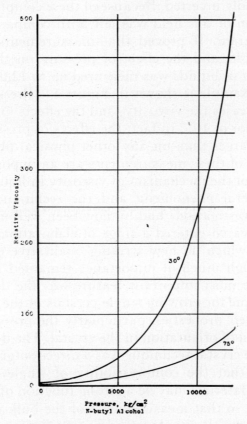

FIG. 51. The effect of pressure on the viscosity of i-butyl alcohol.

tortion of the apparatus, and measurements were made on many substances.

One other major kind of phenomenon remained for investigation: the effect of pressure on the viscosity of liquids. There had been early indications that very large effects might be found in this field, so that the requisite accuracy should be easy to attain; but on the other hand radical changes of technique appeared necessary, such as mounting the entire pressure apparatus so that it would be rapidly and repeatedly inverted. Because of these complications the investigation of this field was left until comparatively late in the program. It proved that measurements were perfectly feasible, and the effect of pressure on the viscosity of a number of liquids was measured up to 12,000 kg/cm^2. A typical example is shown in Figure 51. Pressure almost always increases the viscosity, and the effects may be large, up to a factor of 10^7; in fact, the effects of pressure on viscosity are larger than on any other physical phenomenon. The results of these measurements are an important factor in theories of the mechanism of viscosity in liquids [9].

The general phenomena and the techniques of high-pressure investigations had by now been well mapped out, and the research entered a stage of elaboration and development in which no new striking qualitative effects were found, though much of importance remained to be done. Perhaps the most important feature was the development of a technique for growing single crystals of the metals and studying their properties, particularly the pressure effects, as a function of orientation in the crystal. The development of the single crystal technique was a direct outgrowth of the realization that the compressibility of single crystals of non-cubic materials may be a strong function of crystalline orientation, so that measurements of the bulk modulus of non-cubic crystals are of much less significance than measurements of the linear compressibility in crystallographically well-defined directions.

The several years in which the domain was being consolidated were occupied with the extension of the sort of measurements already made to new elements as they became available, to materials of greater purity, to new classes of liquids, to materials which had some ulterior interest, such as various minerals of the earth's crust, or to new temperatures, as when measurements were extended to liquid-air temperatures. Even after these studies a great deal of importance was still left to do, but the law of diminishing returns was obviously beginning to have something to say and the work began to drag a little. There was one direction in which the domain could obviously be extended, namely, toward increased accuracy. It has always been the experience in physics that new phenomena lie concealed beyond the next decimal place, and these phenomena may be of great and even revolutionary importance, as shown by the whole domain of quantum phenomena. The situation is no different in the high-pressure field; in fact I had early found that for liquids there are small-scale phenomena characteristic of each individual liquid, and had later discovered a great wealth of small-scale phenomena in the behavior of solids with complicated structures, such as alloys with order-disorder transitions [10]. Nevertheless, in spite of the undoubted possibilities, I was not personally of a temperament to look with enthusiasm on the exploitation of the phenomena of the next decimal place, particularly if it was to be done simply by a refinement of the techniques I had already practiced, though there was doubtless room for that. In this view I think I am not greatly different from many of my fellow physicists. One recalls the consternation with which many physicists in the eighteen-nineties contemplated the drab prospect of a future dedicated to the exploration of the next decimal. As a matter of fact, the next decimal place has seldom been exploited except by the development of a radically new technique.

THE RANGE FROM 20,000 TO 50,000 Kg/cm^2

It was obvious that a more satisfactory future, so far as I personally was concerned, was to be found in an extension of the pressure range. For several years I did work in this direction, making measurements in the range between 12,000 and 20,000, which I knew was accessible because I had made my first measurements on water up to 21,000. In this extended range only those phenomena were chosen for investigation which experience in the lower range had indicated would be especially significant, and I did find some important new effects, such as the minimum of resistance of rubidium with pressure and a reversal of the order of the thermal expansion of the alkali metals. The work was, nevertheless, discouraging because of the frequency of rupture of the pressure vessels, destroying not only the vessels but also the complicated apparatus contained in them.

This rupture of the vessels was difficult to understand in the light of my success in reaching this limit some twenty years before, since now I was using some recently developed steels with an ultimate strength 50 per cent greater than had previously been available. I found, however, that it was well known to steel manufacturers that the new high-tensile steels were "temperamental" in that it is difficult to harden complicated shapes without the appearance of hard-

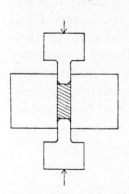

ening cracks. In order, therefore, to utilize the inherent possibilities of the new steels I strove to attain greater simplicity in design, and ultimately arrived at the extreme of simplification by using only one vessel, as shown in Figure 52, in the form of a simple cylinder pierced completely through with a single straight hole [111], without attempt at screw connections of any kind. The sort of thing that could be done with apparatus of such simplicity was obviously limited, but it was possible to measure polymorphic transitions, which involve only the

FIG. 52. Simplified apparatus for reaching pressure somewhat over 25,000 kg/cm².

discontinuity in the motion of the piston as a function of pressure.

This apparatus afforded the solution to one problem that had long attracted attention in this field. Bismuth is abnormal, like water, in that the solid phase has a larger volume than the liquid. The abnormality of water is, however, as already noted, only a transient phenomenon, disappearing at pressures above 2,000. It was to be expected by analogy that solid bismuth under pressure would similarly experience a polymorphic transition to a new solid form denser than the liquid. Search had been made for such a transition, and its discovery had even been announced by one worker, but this later proved to be incorrect. With the new simple pressure apparatus the long-expected transition was found in the neighborhood of 25,000, showing that previous attempts had not used high enough pressures. This same apparatus was capable of a number of similar investigations to pressures of approximately 30,000, a limit set by the strength of both the cylinder and the piston. The prospect offered by a program of research with this equipment was, however, not particularly attractive, because of experimental difficulties. The steel of both receptacle and piston creep under these pressures, with the result that the life of the apparatus is short; either the cylinder bursts or the piston swells and sticks in the hole. Furthermore, due to the slow shortening of the piston the measurements of piston displacement do not give accurate values for the changes of volume.

In view of these unsatisfactory features, I was speculating much at this time on the feasibility of reaching higher pressures by another method. It is obvious enough, and in fact a number of people had independently made the suggestion to me in conversation, that theoretically it is possible to reach any pressure by building a nest of pressure apparatuses one within the other, the pressure in one vessel affording uniform external support for the vessel within it, so that the latter would be capable of withstanding an internal pressure higher than normal by the amount of its external pressure. The difficulty was in a practical working out of the details without excessive complication. Nothing very attractive presented itself, but since this seemed to be what I would eventually have to come to, I did design apparatus of this character and had it constructed. I never tried it, because in the meantime I had hit upon the better solution to be described presently. Here again, too much pertinacity would not have been good tactics.

During all this consideration of the possibility of securing higher pressures another related problem was much in my mind, namely, the production of diamond out of graphite. Measurements were available [12] which indicated that diamond should be thermodynamically stable with respect to graphite at pressures above 30,000, and these were just the pressures I had been using. However, pressures of 30,000 or even 40,000 proved incapable of effecting the transition. This failure might plausibly be attributed to the effect of internal viscosity, which conceivably might be overcome at still higher pressures. It was evident that the pressure for effecting the transition needed to be secured in only a very small region. Now it is known that it is possible to reach very high local stresses in steel properly supported by the surrounding parts, for example, the stress at the point of contact of two crossed knife blades or under the ball of a Brinell hardness tester is very high. A minute flake of graphite placed under a Brinell ball would, therefore, be exposed to pressures considerably higher than previously examined. I experimented with a number of different designs for giving local support to a highly stressed small region and succeeded, with one of these arrangements, in exposing a small bit of graphite to a pressure of 100,000 kg/cm^2 for several hours, but again with no transition to diamond. The attempt was eventually abandoned, and the failure ascribed to the excessive internal friction opposing the reaction. Fortunately the experiments were successful from another point of view, because the solution of the problem of mutual support suggested a design for pressure vessels.

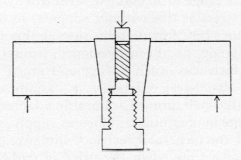

Fig. 53. Illustrating the general principle of the method for giving external support to the pressure vessel in such a way that support increases automatically with the increase of internal pressure.

The method of support for the pressure vessel, which was the outcome of all these attempts, is indicated in Figure 53. The external surface of the vessel is given the form of the frustrum of a cone. When pressure is generated inside the vessel by action of the piston, the vessel is simultaneously pushed into a conical seat, as a stopper is pushed into the neck of a bottle, thus producing an external pressure on the vessel which rises proportionally with the increase of internal pressure. With this method of support it was found feasible to go to pressures of 50,000 kg/cm^2 as a routine matter. This pressure was sufficiently higher than the previous limit to justify the collection of systematic data in this range, even though the lower portion was a duplication of previous measurements. The duplication was not so great as might appear, however, due to the limitations on accuracy at the lower end of the pressure range arising from friction. Furthermore, whenever a pressure range is extended a certain amount of overlapping with the previous work is desirable, since the accuracy of the methods adopted for the new range may be checked in this way.

The design of the pressure vessel in the form of a cone was not the only feature required to make possible the extension of the pressure range to 50,000. No steel will stand as much compressive stress as this without support, so steel pistons were ruled out; but, fortunately, just at this time a new material, carboloy, had been developed, primarily for cutting tools, which was much harder and much stronger in compression than steel. Carboloy, a carbide of tungsten cemented with cobalt, proved admirably adapted to pistons. I was fortunate in obtaining a sufficient supply, through the generosity of the General Electric Company, to make its use feasible at a time when the price of carboloy was so high that its cost would otherwise have been prohibitive.

The experiments possible at 50,000 are naturally more restricted than at lower pressures. In the first place the apparatus is much smaller in size. It is surprising to many people to learn that the higher the pressure the smaller the apparatus. The primary reason for this fact is that only small pieces of steel can be hardened all the way through. There are also secondary reasons to be considered, such as safety, expense, and time, since ruptures naturally become more frequent as the pressure range is increased. The working space in an apparatus for securing a pressure of 50,000 is 0.25 inch in diameter and 0.43 inch long, whereas the apparatus that was used for 12,000 consisted of two or more chambers connected by tubing, each chamber having a capacity of 20 or 30 cm^3. Not only did the size of the maximal apparatus restrict the measurement that could be made in the range up to 50,000, but it restricted the work almost entirely to solids. One reason for this is the fact that almost all substances, except some of the permanent gases, freeze under these pressures at room temperature. Even if the substance remains liquid, perhaps in virtue of subcooling, there is not sufficient room for the complicated packing arrangements necessary for liquids.

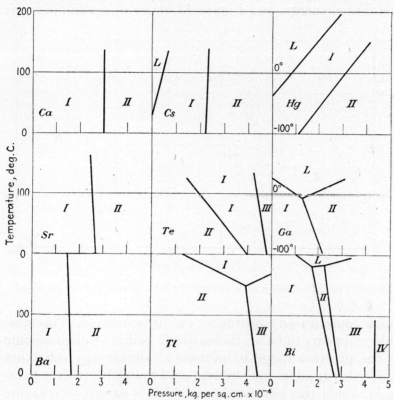

Fig. 54. The phase diagrams (temperature of transition against pressure) for a number of metallic elements.

The necessary simplicity of the apparatus, as just described, practically limits the studies on solids to measurements of the volume compression in terms of the motion of the piston. But, fortunately, there is a great deal that can be usefully done in this range: the simplest thing is the study of polymorphic changes which many substances undergo. The thermodynamic parameters of the transitions of some 75 substances have been determined over this range [13]. Figure 54 shows the transitions of some of the metallic elements, and Figure 55 those of d-camphor, the

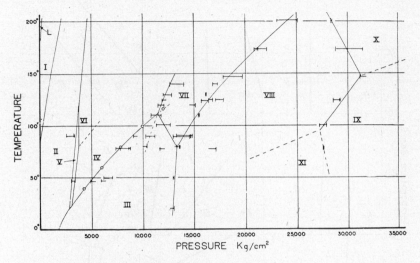

Fig. 55. The phase diagram of d-camphor, the most complicated yet discovered.

most complicated substance yet investigated. Polymorphism appears to be an increasingly common phenomenon as the pressure range is increased; almost any substance selected at random may be expected to exhibit it. It is paradoxical that this phenomenon, which is easiest to measure and which, one would think, involves the most fundamental of the properties of a substance, its space lattice, is theoretically the most difficult to predict or compute. This is because present methods of theoretical computation make the existence of the phenomenon depend on the small difference of large quantities. As a result this mass of experimental material on polymorphism, which anyone must concede has to do with fundamental things, has for the present to be stored like a collection in a museum, waiting for the later moment of illumination, just as spectroscopic data were collected for years before illumination came from later investigations.

The compressibility of solids can also be measured over the range up to 50,000, although with more difficulty, and data have been collected for a considerable number of materials. Liquids too can be measured over that part of the pressure domain in which they are not frozen by the pressure, by the device of sealing them inside a mass of some deformable solid, such as lead, and measuring the over-all compressibility of the whole. In this way the change in compressibility when a substance freezes can be studied over a wide range [14]. The accuracy, of course, is not so great as at lower pressures, since complications arise from the rapidly increasing friction and the distortion of the apparatus. Some of the effects are capricious in sign, so that the accuracy could be increased somewhat if necessary merely by heaping up the measurements. The old problem arises as to just where to make the best compromise between accuracy and extensiveness; this will always be to a certain extent a personal matter, and will also vary with the development of theory and the interest of theoretical physicists in the results. It is fortunate that the error in determinations of compressibility, which have been among the most difficult measurements of all physics at the lower pressures because of the smallness of the effects, becomes less at high pressures with the increase in magnitude.

The experimental arrangements which were used to determine the compressibility of the liquid and solid phases of one substance may also be used to determine the effect of pressure on melting temperature in the range up to nearly 50,000. Previously I had examined the same problem for some 30 or 40 substances in the range up to 12,000 kg/cm^2, and had come to the conclusion that all melting curves are similar in that they rise to indefinite temperatures and pressures and neither end in a critical point nor reach a maximum temperature, as had at one time been supposed.

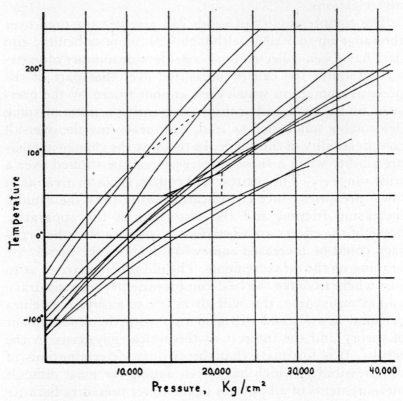

FIG. 56. Melting temperature against pressure for a number of substances. At 15,000 kg/cm² the order of substances, reading from top down, is chloroform, chlorobenzene, chlorobenzene (second modification), water (ice VI), n-butyl alcohol, carbon bisulfide, methylene chloride, n-propyl bromide, ethyl bromide, and ethyl alcohol.

Theoretical physicists had recently reopened the possibility of a critical point, so that it became desirable to reëxamine the question over the wider pressure range now available. A number of the newly determined melting curves are given in Figure 56. Although they are shown as ending in the diagram, this does not indicate a critical point, but merely that, because of experimental difficulties, the curve was not followed further. By combining a study of these curves with the other thermodynamic parameters of the melting, latent heat, and difference of volume, the trend of the phenomenon at pressures beyond those experimentally reached may be studied. The conclusion is a confirmation of that previously reached from measurements in the narrower pressure region, namely, there is no experimental indication that there will ever be either a critical point or a maximum temperature, but all the indications are that the melting curve rises indefinitely with pressure and temperature. This is obviously an important conclusion for geology.

If one is content with pressures below 50,000 it is possible to build more elaborate apparatus employing the same principle of conical support. A greater variety of phenomena may be examined with such an apparatus, and much greater accuracy obtained. I have built apparatus of this type with which pressures of 30,000 may be reached as a routine matter [15], in which the volume is approximately 15 cm^3, and in which pressure is transmitted by a true liquid. The use of a liquid allows the introduction of electrically insulated leads, and this opens the possibility of many different sorts of measurement. A pressure of 30,000 is sufficiently high to justify the inauguration of an extensive program of measurement in this range, particularly since the frequency of breakage has been reduced by the new design to the dimensions of a minor inconvenience.

Some of the questions of special interest in the 30,000-pressure range demand considerable accuracy in the measurements. For instance, there is the change in compressibility of a solid with pressure. Born's theory of solids, as first formulated, had a certain degree of success in calculating the compressibility of salts, such as sodium chloride, but when it came to reproducing the curvature of the curve of volume against pressure it failed by a wide margin. For metals the curvature was so small as to be difficult to measure, but presently the theory was dealing with metals as well as with salts, and it became desirable to obtain data for all these materials with as much accuracy as possible. The accuracy with which a curvature can be measured increases, other things being equal, as the square of the pressure range, so that this effect can be determined at 30,000 six times as accurately as at 12,000. The "other things being equal" includes the accuracy of the measurement of pressure. A preliminary step to entry into this new field was, therefore, just as with the former narrower field, the establishment of methods of measuring pressure with the requisite accuracy, and the location of pressure-fixed points to facilitate the future calibration of pressure gauges. The pressure scale having been fixed and made reproducible to an accuracy of 0.1 per cent, a somewhat similar task had to be done for the measurement of compressibility. The most convenient method of measuring compressibility is a differential method whereby the difference of compression of the substance in question and some standard substance is measured. To convert this sort of measurement into absolute measurement demands a knowledge of the absolute compression of the standard substance. Special methods are needed to determine this. These methods have been developed, and the absolute compressibility of a standard substance, iron, determined over the range to 30,000. The final result of the determination over the wider range of the deviation from linearity of the compressibility of the common metals was a value considerably smaller than had been given by the previous measurements over the narrower pressure range. The new value was much more acceptable to theoretical physicists, who, in the meantime, had been pushing theory to a degree of perfection which gave them considerable confidence in the higher order term.

Right here a significant change in the relation of experiment to theory has occurred since I began my work. At the time when I made my measurements of the effect of pressures up to 12,000 on the electrical resistance of metals or on the compressibility of solids, the theory of these two phenomena was in such a simple state that it was not a hopeless matter for me to attempt to make some contribution to theory in the light of the new experimental material. But by the time that I was measuring compressibility to 50,000 the wave-mechanics theory had developed to such a stage of complexity that it was not possible for me to make a theoretical contribution on the basis of my new data except at the price of completely dropping experimental work and embarking on the extremely problematical course of acquiring sufficient facility in wave mechanics. It is becoming increasingly difficult for the same person to combine theoretical and experimental productivity. For the experimenter this means that he must exert increasingly great care that his work does not degenerate into the hoarding of new data for their own sake.

The problem of maintaining the pressure without rupture of the vessels or leak was not the only problem in extending accurate measurements to the new domain; the question of suitable electrical insulation for the leads was at first most troublesome, the methods of insulation suitable for the former narrower field not being applicable in the extended range. At first the best insulation that I could design usually failed either electrically or mechanically after about two applications of pressure. Under such circumstances the collection of results was very slow because of the necessity for continually taking apart and reassembling the apparatus. I had to decide whether to stop for a systematic development of a more adequate type of insulation or to continue with the measurements, making such changes in the method of insulation from time to time as occurred to me. The latter course, which I took, has, I think, proved to be the better tactics, for now after several years I not only have a considerable accumulation of measurements both on compressibility and on the effect of pressure on electrical resistance, but also have developed an improved method of insulation which permits a number of measurements before reassembly becomes necessary [16]. The method is shown in Figure 57.

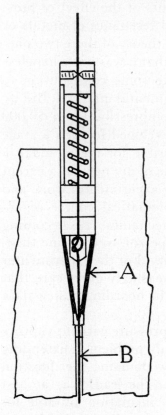

FIG. 57. The method of insulating the leads to stand a pressure of 30,000 kg/cm². *A* is a thin sleeve of pipestone, 0.005 inch thick, *B* is the lead, of piano wire, 0.013 inch in diameter.

THE RANGE ABOVE 50,000 Kg/cm²

Work with the two types of apparatus, that for 50,000 with somewhat less accuracy and restricted to the measurement of simple volume effects, and that for 30,000 with greater accuracy and greater latitude in the effects studied, was carried on side by side for several years. During this time the problem of reaching still higher pressures was continually in the background. It was evident that 50,000 was about the pressure limit possible with the conical type of external support and the carboloy piston. The pressure vessel was just on the point of going to pieces in all directions, like the deacon's one-horse shay; instances were not uncommon in which

the vessel ruptured simultaneously on three mutually per-
pendicular planes. Also the carboloy piston was near its
limit and broke more often than was pleasant. It was increasingly clear that the ultimate nest of pressure vessels
could no longer be sidestepped. With the experience gained
by several years' measurements in the new range this did
not seem as hopeless as at one time, and the problem was
again attacked with more optimism and more prospect of
considerable extension of range than before, because it was
now possible to utilize as the first supporting pressure
30,000 or 50,000 instead of the mere 12,000 that set the
limit earlier.

The first attempts were made with the support afforded
in the 50,000 kg/cm^2 apparatus and were highly encourag-
ing, for they indicated the possibility of reaching pressures
of 200,000 or even more [17]. So large an extension of range,
by considerably more than the support afforded by the
pressure itself, was perhaps more than might have been
hoped for, but it was in line with my early experience that
the usual theories of rupture of heavy vessels under internal
pressure set too low a limit. This large extension was also in
line with observations made by Mr. Griggs [18] in my laboratory in his geophysical studies of the increased strength
and plasticity of rocks and minerals under the support
afforded by hydrostatic pressure. He had found that the
strength was much increased and that the higher the pressure the more rapid the rate of increase, so that it looked
as though it might be exponential. My observations were
consistent with this view, and I accepted them as confirmation. However, the accuracy possible at these new high pressures was so low that it was questionable whether there
would be any great scientific purpose served by extending
the measurements, or whether much would be found that
could be accepted with as much confidence as a simple extrapolation from the lower domain. The reason for the

marked decrease in accuracy was that the "liquid," by which the external supporting "hydrostatic" pressure was exerted, was itself a soft metal, such as lead, indium, or bismuth, and the friction effects were so large as to obscure everything else. It soon became evident that, in order to secure a satisfactory accuracy, the first stage of external support by a hydrostatic pressure would have to be provided in the 30,000 apparatus by a true liquid, in which there was the possibility of accurate measurement through the use of electrically insulated leads.

MEASUREMENT OF PRESSURES

Before this was possible, a "compressometer" had to be developed to measure a thrust on a piston immersed in a fluid under high pressure. This was at last satisfactorily accomplished, and a compound pressure apparatus, consisting of a piston, a cylinder, and a pressure gauge, all completely immersed in the fluid of an outer pressure apparatus, was set up. This is shown in Figures 58 and 59. The inner piston was only $\frac{1}{16}$ inch in diameter, again illustrating how the apparatus becomes smaller with higher pressures. Almost at once it appeared with the use of this more accurate apparatus that the previous estimates of the possibilities in a single stage of support had been set too high. The upper

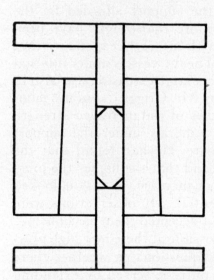

Fig. 58. The miniature apparatus for reaching 100,000 kg/cm². The thrust on the small pistons is measured with an electrical device.

limit is not sharp, because rupture is always capricious, but it is probably not possible under any circumstances, with the materials available, to reach more than 150,000 kg/cm² in the interior of a cylinder with the thrust exerted by a piston, and 125,000 would be a more normal upper limit. With the hindsight afforded by the more accurate measure-

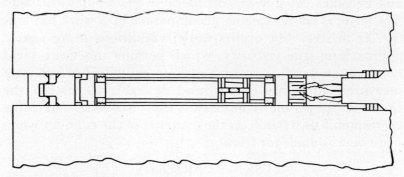

Fig. 59. The miniature pressure apparatus, immersed in the fluid of a larger pressure apparatus to which a pressure of 25,000 kg/cm² or more is applied, with which pressures of 100,000 kg/cm² are reached. The charge is compressed from the two ends by two carboloy pistons. The "cylinder" of the apparatus is compound, consisting of an inner core of carboloy forced into an outer supporting ring of steel.

ments, a reinspection of the previous results, in which support was provided in the 50,000 apparatus, indicated an equally plausible way of interpreting the results so that there was now no inconsistency with the new limit of 150,000. It also appeared in the light of the more accurate measurements that the supposed exponential increase of strength with supporting pressure was illusory, and that the increase of strength is at least approximately linear in the supporting pressure for the materials used for piston and cylinder, a result which ordinary physical intuition, I think, will find more congenial. In any event, there is an increase of strength under supporting pressure and there is, therefore, a gain in supporting the apparatus by external hydrostatic pressure of more than the supporting pressure itself.

There is also a notable increase in ductility, as shown by the specimens in Figure 60.

The limit of 125,000, just mentioned, has to be further cut down when accurate measurements are required because of the slow creep of the carboloy piston. Under high supporting pressure carboloy loses its ordinary brittleness and becomes capable of considerable plastic deformation. The latter is not noticeably accompanied by a work hardening, as in steel, but occurs under conditions more nearly approaching true viscosity, which permits indefinite yield when the pressure is continued long enough. For accurate measurement it has been found desirable to restrict the thrust on the piston to approximately 110,000 kg/cm^2; this corresponds to 100,000 on the contents of the cylinder when allowance is made for friction.

USE OF CARBOLOY

The possibility is now open, therefore, of making simple volume measurements up to pressures of 100,000 and studying polymorphic transitions and compressions in this range. When I started on such a program, it soon developed that accurate results were going to be difficult for another reason, namely, the very large distortion of the cross section of the steel containers under pressure, which becomes greater than 10 per cent, with an unknown and increasing uncertainty as to the proper way to calculate the correction. The obvious remedy was to make the pressure vessel of some material with much higher elastic constants, so that it would be less deformable. For this purpose the only material with a sufficient gain in elastic constants appeared to be carboloy itself, but at first this seemed to me to be ruled out for two reasons: the impossibility of making carboloy cylinders and the fact that carboloy would be expected to rupture in tension more easily than steel, its superior strength normally being in the direction of compression. However, on

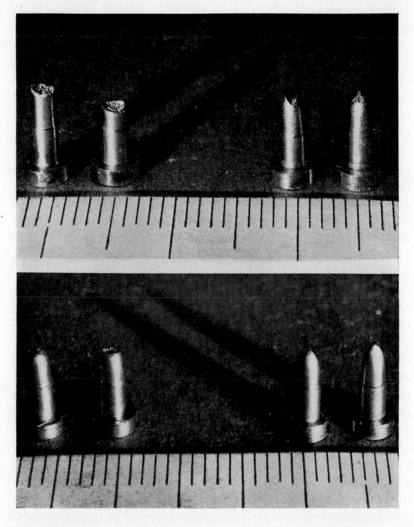

FIG. 60. The effect of pressure in increasing the ductility of steel. Above are shown two different grades of steel broken in tension at atmospheric pressure. Below are specimens of the same grades of steel broken while immersed in a liquid exposed to 25,000 kg/cm². The approximately 100 per cent reduction in the size of the specimen on the right is especially striking.

reflection and inquiry it appeared that neither of these considerations might be decisive. Basset [19] in France had published results in which he had obtained high pressures in carboloy cylinders with external supporting jackets of shrunk-on steel. It also turned out that a technique had been developed in this country, just in time for my experiments, of drilling accurate holes in carboloy, so that the cylinders could be made. As far as the rupture of carboloy under internal pressure was concerned it was obvious that my conditions were more favorable than Basset's, because the external supporting pressure would, in virtue of differential compression between carboloy and steel jacket, afford an additional differential pressure on the carboloy cylinder. I hoped that this extra factor would be sufficient to give the additional strength needed to get beyond Basset's pressures by the amount desired.

The first trial was successful, as it so seldom is. The distortion was found to be only one-third of that for steel, and this can be calculated with less uncertainty than in the other measurements. The over-all accuracy is perhaps about 2 per cent. As so often occurs, one has to put up with a diminished accuracy in extending the range, but the accuracy is great enough to permit results of value and is probably within any present-day theoretical demands. With this apparatus I have started on a program of measurements up to 100,000 and already have values for the volume compressions and polymorphic transitions of some seventeen elements [20] and a number of simple compounds in the new range. The curves for several of these are shown in Figure 61. There are a number of new polymorphic forms. For example, bismuth has a new form, making its phase diagram strikingly similar to that of water, and antimony has a form looked for at lower pressures, but without success, because of the close resemblance between the lattice structures of the ordinary forms of bismuth and antimony.

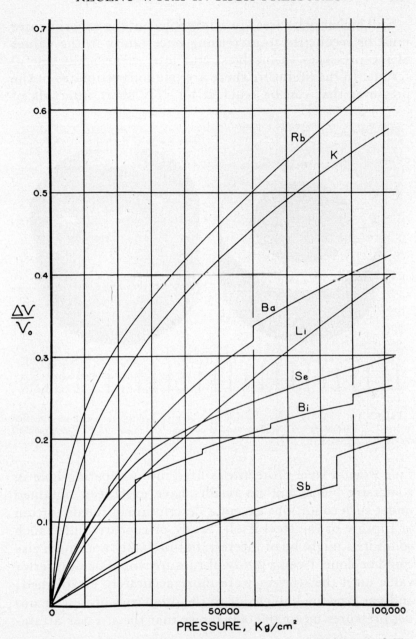

FIG. 61. The volume compressions of several elements up to 100,000 kg/cm². The breaks in some of the curves indicate polymorphic transitions.

Still higher pressures are attainable, but the experimenter must be reconciled to increasing uncertainty in the values of the pressures themselves, and less scientifically useful results. In the literature there are fabulous estimates of the pressures that can be reached for very short intervals of

Fig. 62. Two pieces of carboloy which have been pushed together with an intensity of stress of 400,000 kg/cm² on their area of contact. The radial cracks were produced on *release* of pressure.

time when a steel projectile is fired into a tapering hole in a massive block, but no results have ever been obtained under such conditions except a description of the distortion or rupture of the steel itself. Study of rupture under such conditions might be of interest, but probably not much else could be done. Even a study of rupture would be of inferior value until the stresses were more accurately established; and our growing knowledge of the properties of matter under pressures up to 100,000 shows that the stresses attainable under such conditions have been much overestimated and are no greater than may be reached under better controlled conditions in other ways.

It now appears that certain very limited studies can be made at controlled and maintained pressures materially above 100,000. It will be recalled that I subjected a miniature piece of graphite to a pressure of 100,000 in an apparatus entirely composed of steel. It is evident that higher pressures can be secured if a miniature form of such an apparatus is subjected to one stage of external support by hydrostatic pressure in the apparatus for 30,000, and that still higher pressures may be anticipated if the miniature apparatus is made of carboloy instead of steel. This is essentially what I have done, with certain modifications. Figure 62 shows two pieces of carboloy that were used in an experiment of this sort. Pressures of 400,000 kg/cm^2 or more can be reached in this way on minute flakes of various materials [21]; these flakes are large enough so that after exposure to such pressures they can be examined by Xrays to determine whether there has been any permanent alteration, such as the alteration from yellow to black phosphorus occurring at 12,000. Seven or eight substances selected as most likely to give positive results because of their position in the periodic table have been examined in this way but with negative results. Even at this pressure graphite is not changed to diamond. It is probable that Tammann was right and that if a certain transformation is not effected by a moderate pressure in excess of the pressure of the thermodynamically reversible transition, it will not be effected by any pressure, no matter how high, the tendency to the transformation passing through a maximum with increasing pressure.

Interesting examples of rupture take place under these very high stresses. It would doubtless be of value to study them systematically, because they can be measured with some accuracy, but as yet I have not had a chance to embark on such a program. The only other thing in sight to do with these very high pressures is to search for permanent transformations. In view of the negative results so far attained, I shall probably leave this field in abeyance until there are more positive indications from the theoretical side as to the most probable places to look for such effects. The next step in the direction of still higher pressures is obviously two stages of external support, but this at present seems an incalculable distance in the future.

For References see p. 299.

RECENT DEVELOPMENTS IN POWER GENERATION

By LIONEL S. MARKS

Harvard University

APPLICATIONS OF POWER

THE most important applications of power units are for the generation of electricity and for transportation. The electricity produced in power stations, though used in part for the production of light and heat, is primarily a medium for the transmission of power for the operation of machinery and for transportation in subways and on electrified railways. The power units for transportation in locomotives, ships, automobiles, and aircraft make very different demands upon the designer. A power unit satisfactory for any one of these services is generally unsatisfactory for any of the others. The recent project of applying truck engines for the propulsion of a new type of cargo ship (the "Sea Otter") is justified only by the existence of greater facilities for the rapid manufacture of truck engines than for the manufacture of marine engines.

The use to which power is put dictates the dominant characteristics of the power-generating device. For generating electricity in a power plant, the determining consideration, after ensuring reliability and safety, is the minimum total cost per unit of power; bulk and weight are of minor interest. The thermal efficiency of the unit is not of controlling importance, although the endeavor to improve that efficiency has been a major factor in the development of the power station. The cost of fuel in such stations is usually not more than one-tenth of the total cost of electricity to the consumer. Consequently, an improvement of fuel economy of 10 per cent would decrease the cost to the consumer by not much more than 1 per cent, even if such improvement could be obtained without additional first cost.

In locomotives, marine engines, and automobiles, economy, while of interest, is not a deciding factor; compactness and weight have to be considered also. For aircraft the maximum must be attained in compactness and lightness; the fuel economy is of importance but only because it determines the weight of fuel which must be carried.

Reliability is seldom a first consideration and is frequently obtained by duplication. It is most important for central power plants, less important for transportation units. Even in the airplane, reliability is not the deciding consideration and is sacrificed in part in order to obtain low weight, compactness, and efficiency. The actual degree of reliability is, however, high in all types of power units.

SOURCES OF POWER

The possible sources of power are the gravitational pull of the moon, the internal energy of the earth, and solar energy.

The gravitational pull of the moon produces the tides and it is possible to obtain useful work from the tides in a few specially favored localities. Such power always entails great first cost and, as it is discontinuous, it requires arrangements for the storage of power if the power demand is continuous. There are very few places where tidal power can be utilized economically. The Passamaquoddy area is certainly not among these. The estimate by Jeffries [1] of the tidal drag on the earth is 1.4×10^9 kw. which is not much more than the total power that could be developed by all the automobiles of the United States operating at full load.

The internal energy of the earth is utilizable in those places where high-pressure steam emerges continuously, but it is of such infrequent occurrence as to be of no real importance. No hopeful practical suggestions have been made for more general utilization of the internal energy of the earth.

SOLAR ENERGY

Solar energy is the only important source of power. It is the cause of winds, of rain, and of plant growth. The solar energy of earlier ages is stored in coal, petroleum, and natural gas. Solar energy of recent times is stored in vegetable and animal matter and in water above sea level.

Certain energy sources are immediately available for doing work, as in water wheels or windmills. In such cases it is in general conceivable that all the available energy should be converted into work. Actually, there are losses from friction or other causes, but these may be reduced indefinitely as progress is made in the mechanic arts; efficiencies of 90 per cent are usual in such cases. Heat is not available energy, and some form of heat engine is necessary for its transformation into work. The efficiency of this process in actual engines is less than 40 per cent.

The value of an energy source for power generation depends in addition on certain other characteristics. The energy may be concentrated, as in a high waterfall, or diffuse as in a slow-moving stream; it may be continuous as in a waterfall, or intermittent as with sunlight or wind; it may be storable as with water in reservoirs, or not storable as with the wind. These and other characteristics of sources of energy have a controlling influence on their value for doing the daily work of the world.

Wind Power. An estimate of the order of magnitude of the energy of the winds can be made in various ways. The global wind power is probably of the order of magnitude of about 10^{12} kw. This is equivalent to several hundred times the heat of combustion of all the coal mined during the year, but is only about 1 per cent of the solar energy reaching the earth's surface.

The winds of the world are not in general usable, since they extend to heights of many miles and are present over large areas of the seas and in the polar areas. In addition, they are usually variable, intermittent, and of low intensity. Nevertheless, they have been most valuable in the past for the generation of small amounts of power, for purposes such as grinding corn and pumping water, which do not demand continuity of service. The old-fashioned Dutch-type windmill with four sails, each 24 ft. long and 6 ft. wide, develops less than 5 hp. in a 20-mile wind.

For the continuity necessary for modern industrial uses, wind power must be tied in with some steady source of power, such as a steam plant or a water-power plant with limited storage, so that the power which it generates may save fuel or water. For satisfactory operation, such a windmill must be located at the top of a hill, on a site of fairly constant winds of good velocity. The first plant of this type, shown in Figure 63, is now being put into operation in Vermont on a mountain summit, 2,000 ft. above sea level. The unit is a two-bladed propeller-type windmill [2] of 1,000 kw. capacity with an over-all diameter of 175 ft. and with blades 16 ft. in maximum width. The blades are designed in accordance with modern aerodynamic theory and have a variable pitch (as in airplane propellers), controlled by governor action so as to maintain a constant speed of 30 rpm. for wind speeds from 15 to 70 mph. Above 70 mph. the blades come to a feathering position and the mill ceases to rotate. It develops full power with a wind velocity of 30 mph. or more. Adequate winds for driving this unit blow about 60 per cent of the time. Full power should be obtainable about 50 per cent of the time.

Water Power. Of the solar energy arriving at the earth's crust about one-half is used in evaporation; 100,000 cubic

Fig. 63. Windmill power plant in Vermont.

miles of water are evaporated by it every year. Of this amount about two-thirds is evaporated from the oceans, and more than half of it falls there as rain. The volume falling on land surfaces is about 45,000 cubic miles per year, of which about one-fifth reaches the rivers. If this water were available at an average elevation of 50 ft. above sea level, it could yield an output of 5×10^{12} kw. The actual world water power appears to be about 7×10^7 kw.; the economically feasible water power is probably not more than 10 times this quantity, or about 10^9 kw.

The development of a water-power plant usually demands high initial expenditures but the operating costs are low. At those localities in the United States where the first costs are low enough to make water power competitive with steam power, such plants have generally been built by private enterprise. The recent large developments by the Federal Government at Tennessee Valley, Bonneville, and Grand Coulee have had to rely for their economic justification on their incidental values for irrigation, flood control, navigation, and the like. Under these circumstances, it is impossible to allocate costs satisfactorily to the various services. Moreover, the design and operation should be different for the various services. Flood control is best obtained by empty reservoirs, but power requires full reservoirs. Power can be obtained most economically with high dams, but navigation and irrigation can often be best served by a sequence of low dams. In some cases power is charged only with the cost of the power plant, while the much greater costs of the dams, reservoirs, etc., are charged to the other purposes. This has resulted in much confused thinking about the cost of hydraulic power.

In earlier times water power was used principally for grinding grain and for pumping water to higher levels. It had to be used where it occurred, since the means for power transmission were not available; the only source of continuous power away from a water wheel until the eighteenth century was animal power.

The water power of the United States is about one-third of the total central-station power, and is used chiefly for the generation of electrical energy. The efficiency of this conversion at rated load is very high. The turbine itself may have an efficiency of 93 per cent or over, and the electric generator may have an efficiency of over 96 per cent.

FIG. 64. Kaplan turbine.

The product of these two may be over 90 per cent. These efficiencies are obtainable with the best installations with all types of turbines at rated load, but with partial loads or with varying hydraulic head, the efficiency may be considerably lower. In the comparatively recent Kaplan turbine, as shown in Figures 64 and 65, which is of the propeller type, adapted to heads of not more than 70 ft., a high efficiency is maintained through a wide range of operating conditions by making the propeller blades rotatable about their axes so that their pitch can be modified [3]. This is standard practice in airplane propellers and, as stated above, is used in the new type of windmill. The largest turbines of this type built in this country are the 66,000 hp.

units at Bonneville Dam, which have an outside diameter of
the runner of 23 ft. 4 in., a hub diameter of 10 ft., run at

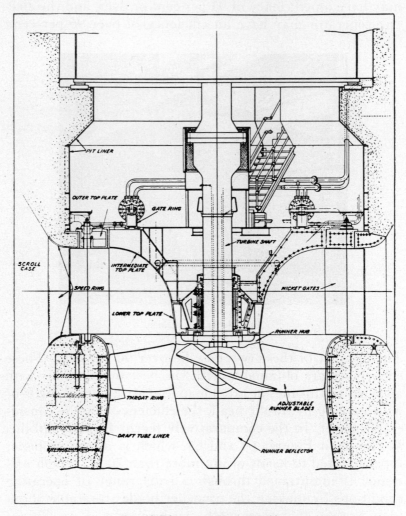

FIG. 65. Diagram of Kaplan turbine.

75 rpm., and operate with an average head of about 54 ft.
The runner is essentially similar to a ship's propeller, to an

airplane propeller, and to the windmill already shown. The Bonneville Dam runners have each 5 blades. The total weight of the rotating parts is over 1,000 tons; their support by practically frictionless bearings is one of the triumphs of modern mechanical science.

FIG. 66. Stator of the Francis reaction-type water wheel.

The largest water wheel in this country is of the Francis reaction type and has over 108,000 hp. capacity. The picture of the stator of its electric generator gives some impression of its size (Fig. 66).

Solar Energy. The solar energy [4] arriving at the outside of the earth's atmosphere on a plane normal to the sun's rays is about 1.1 kw. per sq. yd.; of this only about 43 per cent, or $\frac{1}{2}$ kw. per sq. yd., reaches the earth's surface. The total solar energy arriving at the earth's surface is at the rate of 7.5×10^{13} kw. To give some meaning to this astronomical figure, it may be compared with the heat of combustion of all the petroleum which has been deposited in the earth's crust. A liberal estimate, making large allowance for future discoveries, indicates that the volume of this petroleum is certainly less than one trillion barrels. The heat of combustion of this quantity of petroleum is about equal to the solar energy arriving at the earth's crust in half a day. A similar estimate of the coal in the earth's crust indicates that its heat of combustion is equivalent to the solar energy arriving at the earth's surface in less than six months.

Nearly all of the incident solar energy is converted to low-temperature heat and is of small value for power generation. An exceedingly minute fraction is converted into the available energy of winds and of water as a result of the uncontrolled convection of heated air currents, of evaporation, and of condensation. A very small but, to us, all-important fraction of the solar energy is caught by photosynthetic processes in growing plants and is there stored as the heat of combustion of the plant. Under certain circumstances plant material has become coal or petroleum and as such has been stored for long periods. Usually, unless the plant material is harvested and utilized by human agency, it oxidizes rapidly and becomes carbon dioxide and water again.

Solar Motors. It is possible to receive the sun's rays on properly shaped and controlled reflecting surfaces, to concentrate these rays on a steam boiler or equivalent device, to generate steam with them, and to use this steam in some form of steam engine. A number of such "solar engines" have been built and installed in localities, such as Egypt and Arizona, where there is maximum sunshine. Solar engines can deliver available energy only during the sunshine hours and then only in an amount which varies with the sun's position; they cover a large area for the amount of power delivered and have a first cost per unit of power which is usually prohibitive. While functioning they may convert into useful work as much as 3 per cent of the solar energy falling on the area which the reflectors occupy. If the demand for power is continuous, there must be added some device for storing power, and such devices are costly and inefficient. There are not many places in which a solar engine could be economically justified.

Photosynthesis. The photosynthetic process is actually the most efficient natural starting point for converting solar energy into work. Under favorable circumstances [5] it is possible to store as heat of combustion of plants as much as 1.5 per cent of the solar energy which falls during the growing months on a planted area. This is the performance obtained in the growth of corn during the three summer months in a Midwest area. In the tropics, with proper selection of plants, this performance might be repeated two or three times per year. This would make it possible to store about 1 per cent of the total annual solar energy falling on such areas. With large-scale operation, about 25 per cent of the heat of combustion of plants could be converted into work, giving an overall efficiency of conversion from solar energy to useful work of about one-fourth of 1 per cent. This may seem small, but amounts to a continuous supply of work at the rate of 5 kw. per acre in certain tropical areas.

HEAT ENGINES

Actual heat engines operate with fluid working substances. In internal-combustion engines, such as gasoline engines and Diesel engines, the products of combustion of the fuel function directly in the cylinders. The alternative method is to have the products of combustion evaporate a liquid, separated from the combustion gases by metal surfaces, and to use the vapor as a working substance. The liquid is usually water, in which case the engine is called a steam engine or turbine, but other liquids can be used.

The efficiency of a heat engine is primarily a function of the temperature range. Under the most favorable circumstances all heat additions are at the maximum temperature of the cycle and all heat rejections are at the minimum temperature. The minimum temperature is fixed by the temperature of the available cooling medium (water or air) and may be taken as 80° F. With a maximum temperature of 1,000° F. the ultimate possible percentage of the heat of combustion that can be converted into work (Carnot efficiency) is 63 per cent. The condition that all heat be supplied at the maximum temperature can be approximated to by the process of evaporation in vapor engines; in internal combustion engines heat is usually added until the gas reaches its maximum temperature, but no appreciable amount of heat is added at that temperature.

The maximum practicable temperature in a vapor engine is controlled by two conditions: (1) the diminution in strength and reliability of metals at high temperatures, and (2) the physical properties of the vapor.

The strength of the metals suitable for use in power plants falls off rapidly at temperatures above about 700° F. but a number of alloys have sufficient strength at 1,000° F. to make operation at that temperature commercially feasible. The principal difficulty is that "creep" begins to be important at these temperatures. Creep [6] is the slow deformation which occurs in metals subjected to a stress which is within the elastic limit. Experience indicates that a stretch of 1 per cent in 10 years is permissible in certain structures; in others not more than 0.1 per cent can be tolerated. The maximum permissible stretch determines the life of the structure. The creep of a part subjected to high temperature will usually deform attached structures, such as pipes, but it is found that these will generally undergo enough plastic deformation under the stresses so set up as to relieve themselves of excessive stress. The addition of molybdenum and chromium to steels increases their creep strength. The limit of temperature in present-day use for turbine parts is 1,000° F. but current practice favors 900-950° F. For boiler tubes in which constancy of form is not necessary, higher temperatures are practicable.

The critical temperature of steam is about 705° F., and the corresponding pressure 3,200 lbs. per sq. in. As the latent heat of a vapor is zero at the critical temperature, it is obvious that no heat would be supplied at the maximum temperature if saturated steam at the critical temperature were used in an engine. Furthermore, it would become so wet on expansion as to reduce greatly the efficiency of the engine. There is in operation one large steam-turbine plant [7] using steam at 2,300 lbs. per sq. in. (which corresponds to a saturation temperature of 655° F.) with the steam superheated to 940° F. This plant has a thermal efficiency of 33.5 per cent from coal to electrical output and has given the best performance of any steam plant. It is not likely to be improved upon appreciably, since further increases in pressure and temperature of the steam would yield but little increase in efficiency. The efficiency figure is the product of the efficiencies of the furnace and boiler, of the steam engine, and of the electric generator. In the best modern practice, the combined efficiency of the furnace (in achieving complete combustion of the fuel) and of the boiler (in transmitting the heat of combustion to the water, to the steam, and to the air arriving at the furnace) is in excess of 90 per cent. The efficiency of the electric generator in converting mechanical energy into electrical energy may be as high as 97 per cent. Assuming these values, the efficiency of the turbine under consideration in converting heat into mechanical energy is about 38 per cent and, as the theoretical efficiency of this turbine is about 45 per cent, the turbine is doing about 82 per cent of what is possible for it.

The steam turbine is superior to the steam engine in many respects. It is is of higher efficiency, since it can utilize high superheat and can be operated with a much better vacuum; it is much more compact, can be built in much larger sizes, operates at higher speeds (thereby reducing the size of the electric generators which it drives) and has much lower labor, lubrication, and maintenance costs. It has supplanted the steam engine everywhere except in locomotives and a few smaller applications where the reciprocating motion or the low speed or high torque of the engine are of special importance.

Mercury-Steam Turbine. The efficiency of a steam turbine is limited by the properties of its working substance. A desirable fluid would have a critical temperature well above 1,000° F., a freezing point well below 80° F., and commercially practicable pressures at those temperatures. In addition, the fluid should be stable, not too costly, and not corrosive.

There is no such fluid. Thermodynamic theory indicates, however, that a heat engine cycle using a series of two or more fluids may have the same efficiency as a heat engine cycle using a single fluid through the same temperature range. To obtain the same efficiency, it is necessary that the first fluid, on condensing, should use its latent heat in evaporating the second fluid without temperature drop. As the limitation with steam is at the high temperature end, it is desirable in a binary vapor system to precede it by some other fluid. The best fluid for this purpose is mercury. At 1,000° F. the pressure of mercury vapor is 180 lbs. per sq. in.; on expansion to 1 lb. per sq. in. the temperature becomes 458° F. At that temperature steam has a pressure of 460 lbs. per sq. in. and on expanding to 80° F. its pressure becomes 0.5 lb. per sq. in. In other words, the complete range from 1,000° F. to 80° F. can be covered by mercury expanding from 180 to 1 lb. per sq. in., followed by steam expanding from 460 lbs. to 0.5 lb. per sq. in. In practice, it is

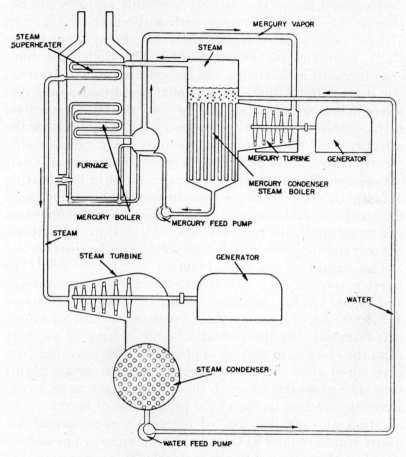

FIG. 67. Diagram of the mercury-steam turbine.

necessary to have a temperature drop between the two fluids of about 50° F. in order that the transfer of heat from the condensing mercury to the evaporating water should proceed with sufficient rapidity, and this reduces the possible efficiency and modifies the pressure ranges of the two fluids (Fig. 67).

The mercury-steam turbine after thirty years of intensive development has at last become a reliable and efficient device [8]. It is now operating with a thermal efficiency of 37.5 per cent, which is higher than that of any other power plant, including the Diesel engine. The difficulties have been formidable. Mercury was thought to be inert to steel, but it was found that, under boiler conditions, iron dissolves in mercury. In addition, mercury does not wet a steel surface, and consequently there is a vapor film between the mercury and the steel which results in a considerably greater temperature difference between the two than exists between steel and water. This has resulted in overheating of boiler tubes. After much investigation, it has been found that with the addition of minute quantities of magnesium and titanium to the mercury, the steel surface is perfectly wetted, and the steel is no longer soluble in the mercury.

The weight of mercury required is considerable. The latest plant, yielding 20,000 kw. for the mercury turbine and 30,000 kw. for the steam turbine, had an initial charge of 390,000 lbs. of mercury. Both for economy and for safety, it is essential that there should be no leakage of mercury from the system, so that no appreciable additional mercury is required after the first charge. If mercury-steam plants should be generally adopted, there would have to be a considerable increase in the world production of mercury. An addition of 1,000,000 kw. of mercury-steam turbine capacity would require 8,000,000 lbs. of mercury. The normal world production is only about 9,000,000 lbs. per year, and most of this is used for various industrial processes. The weight of mercury used is about 8 lbs. per net kw. and at present costs would add about 8 per cent to the initial cost of the plant. Its economic justification depends, of course, on many other factors also.

The operation of the mercury turbine demands unusual precautions, such as the use throughout of welded containing structures for the prevention of leakage. A recently developed optical-type mercury detector gives clear indica-

Fig. 68. Outdoor mercury-turbine plant.

tions of a concentration of mercury vapor in the chimney gases of as little as 1 part per 100 million. The danger from possible escape of mercury vapor was reduced in earlier installations by enclosing the equipment in an outer casing, inside of which a slight vacuum was maintained. Another procedure is to erect the plant outdoors with no enclosing building as illustrated in Figure 68. An extension of this practice to steam turbines is one of the latest developments and results in considerable saving in first cost. Figure 69

FIG. 69. Turbine-generator set designed for open-air operation.

shows a turbine-generator set designed for the open air and now being installed in California.

Electric Generators. In addition to the developments in the turbine, the other elements in steam plants have also undergone marked improvement and modification. The design of electric generators has been improved so that it is now possible to operate them at a speed of 3,600 rpm. for capacities up to 75,000 kw. A large generator at this speed may have centrifugal forces, tending to explode the rotor, which may be of the order of 400 million pounds. The increase in speed has resulted in a great reduction in size and weight. In addition they are now completely enclosed and operate in an atmosphere of hydrogen. The capacity of the generator can be increased 25 per cent or more by this means, since the limit of capacity of a generator is fixed by the maximum temperature which it is permitted to attain and the rise in temperature is kept down by the high conductivity of the hydrogen. In addition, the low density of the gas reduces greatly the frictional windage loss.

Steam Generators. Boilers have altered so much in recent years that even their name has been changed. They are now called steam generators and are built in units with capacity up to 1 million pounds of steam per hour. Formerly, the boiler consisted mainly of tubes through which water flowed and over which the gaseous products of combustion passed. Such convection surface has practically disappeared in large steam generators. Its place is taken by radiation surface. The furnace, instead of being surrounded by firebrick refractories, is now enclosed by vertical steel tubes up which water flows and in which steam is generated. This has greatly increased the life of the furnace and its freedom from troubles. In addition, it permits and demands furnace temperatures which would have melted the old refractory walls in very short time. The high temperatures are obtained by preheating the air and admitting only a slight excess of air. With the development of satisfactory devices for burning powdered coal, it is now possible to extend considerably the range of coals satisfactory for any given plant and to burn coal with a degree of control that previously was possible only with liquid or gaseous fuels. Rapid starting and stopping are possible, with resultant economies. The high temperatures now used have been made practicable by the development of special alloy steels. New alloys containing columbium may permit still further improvements.

Modern boilers are mainly welded structures. Steam drums, which may be 5 in. thick, 5 ft. in diameter and 40 ft. long, are always welded. The rate of heat transfer is so great that the natural circulation of the water, on which reliance was formerly placed, is now being aided by forced circulation and in some cases by once-through flow. In this last case, there is no continuous body of water in which circulation can be set up, but water is forced past the heating surfaces by the feed pump and a mixture of water and steam discharges into the steam drum. The steam separates out and goes to the superheater, while the water, with the addition of condensate equal to the weight of liberated steam, is forced again through the boiler.

Modern boiler furnaces are of enormous size. In large plants they may be 60 ft. in height and may have a volume of 40,000 cubic ft. With vertical tube walls, they give somewhat the impression of the nave of a Gothic cathedral. The large size permits time enough for the completion of combustion before the gases come into contact with cooling surfaces. Over 90 per cent of the heat of perfect combustion of the coal may be absorbed in the various heating surfaces before the products of combustion are finally rejected to the atmosphere.

INTERNAL-COMBUSTION ENGINES

Internal-Combustion Engines. In internal-combustion engines combustion occurs inside the cylinders, the products of combustion doing work directly on moving elements. There is no necessary relation between the temperature and pressure of the gases. The maximum temperature is that reached during combustion and this may be 3,000° F. or higher and is well above the melting temperature of the containing walls. The possibility of operation results from the fact that the high temperatures are reached for a brief instant only, and also from the continuous active cooling of the cylinders from the outside.

Internal-combustion engines are of two main types: (1) the explosion engine used in automobiles, in which an explosive mixture is taken into the cylinder, compressed, and ignited, and (2) the compression-ignition engine, or Diesel engine, in which air alone is taken into the cylinder and compressed to a pressure so high that the resulting temperature is sufficient to ignite finely-atomized fuel, injected at or near the end of the compression.

Internal-combustion engines offer many advantages over external-combustion or vapor engines. As they do not need boilers, condensers, feed pumps, heaters, etc., they are much more compact and of lighter weight. They are instantly available and do not have to be supplied with large quantities of water. The possibilities of high thermal efficiency are greater because the working substance operates at a much higher temperature. This higher efficiency is actually realized in smaller units but not in large units, as already indicated in the discussion of the mercury turbine.

Airplane Engines. As a result of developments covering many years, the automobile engine has reached a striking degree of reliability and economy, but it has remained for the demands of the airplane engine to lift the explosion engine to a new level of performance. The airplane engine is undoubtedly the most exigent of all engines; it demands reliability, economy, light weight, and compactness in the highest degree. These requirements may be conflicting as, for example, lightest weight and greatest reliability, and consequently a compromise has to be accepted. The net result is probably the most remarkable achievement of the engineer. In its most advanced forms the airplane engine weighs not more than 1 lb. per hp. developed, has very low fuel consumption, has a life of about 500 hrs. between major overhauls, and is very compact. It consists always of a considerable number of cylinders arranged either in a circle or in line. The cylinder diameter cannot exceed 6 in. since the center of the piston has to be kept at a tolerable temperature by a radial flow of heat to the walls.

The work done per cycle in a given cylinder is a function of the amount of heat liberated during the combustion process. The limit is fixed by the weight of oxygen present and not by the weight of fuel injected. Maximum power is obtained when all the oxygen is used up. The oxygen will not be used up if the stoichiometrically correct quantity of fuel is present, since there is not time enough in the cycle for equilibrium to be reached and some of the fuel will be incompletely burned. For the combustion of all the oxygen and the development of maximum power, an excess of fuel must be present and this is wasteful; for maximum economy a stoichiometric deficiency of fuel must exist with consequently reduced power.

The engine power depends on the engine speed. At high speed there is a short time for each admission of charge to the cylinder (at 2,400 rpm. this is $\frac{1}{80}$ sec.), and this demands a high velocity of flow and results in a low admission pressure in the cylinder. There is always an optimum speed of the engine beyond which the diminution of weight of charge admitted per cycle to the cylinder more than offsets the increase in the number of cycles per minute. This is the speed at which the engine runs.

The power developed per cylinder can be increased by supercharging, that is, by forcing the charge in under pressure. With supercharge to 2 atmospheres' pressure, the weight of oxygen in the cylinder can be doubled as compared with operation without supercharging. This procedure is essential for maintaining airplane speed at altitudes where the barometer is one-half or one-third of that at sea level, and is now universal practice for military planes. At the present time, doubling the engine power by supercharging is about the practical limit. High supercharging must be used cautiously at low altitudes. Most engines cannot be operated with full supercharge at sea level for more than a few minutes without wrecking the engine.

The avoidance of detonation has been one of the outstanding difficulties in the development of the airplane engine. Detonation is an explosion phenomenon familiar to automobile operators as the cause of the sharp metallic knocking noise which may occur when climbing a steep hill with open throttle. The automobilist knows that it can be reduced or avoided by using certain special gasolines. After many years of intensive research the phenomenon is still but poorly understood. It occurs toward the end of the explosion and appears to result from the instantaneous combustion of the as-yet-unburned fraction of the charge, in contrast with the progressive combustion of normal operation. The detonation is so fast that a high local pressure builds up and is exerted on the adjacent portion of the cylinder head. The difference between the explosions of dynamite and gunpowder is analogous.

To attain maximum work and maximum economy from a given cylinder, it is necessary to operate with the maximum possible compression ratio. Detonation limits this ratio. Consequently it has been necessary to discover nondetonating fuels. The value of the fuel in resisting detonation is measured by an arbitrarily standardized procedure and is stated as an octane number. An octane number of 75 is excellent for automobile use; an octane number of 100 is normally required for fighter planes. The greatest single factor in the improvement of the airplane engine in recent years has been the development of fuels of octane numbers of 100 or over.

Shortly after the end of the last war, the writer produced a book on *The Airplane Engine* and indulged in some forecasts as to its future. He predicted that the airplane engine of the future would be a Diesel engine because the fuel consumption of the Diesel was only about two-thirds that of the explosion engine, and its substitution would increase the radius of action of the airplane by about 50 per cent. This forecast has been falsified by the development of high octane fuels which have reduced the fuel consumption of the explosion engine almost to that of the Diesel engine.

Since the Diesel engine is at present somewhat heavier than an explosion engine of the same power, its use would not result in an appreciable decrease in total weight of engine and fuel for the same power and radius of action. Current difficulties with the ignition systems of explosion engines at very high altitudes may favor the Diesel engine and may result in its use under those conditions.

In order to obtain light weight, the design stresses in the parts of an airplane engine have been increased until they probably exceed those of any other machine; the factor of safety for the various parts, which is intended to cover defects or unforeseen loadings and which ordinarily has a value of 4 or 5, is sometimes reduced almost to unity and is in general not greater than 2. Not only are the loadings heavy, but they are repeated with great frequency. For example, a connecting rod may be loaded up to 20 tons 20 times per second, or 36 million times during the 500-hour period which is now the interval before a major overhauling with the best American engines. Under these circumstances the permissible stress per square inch must not exceed a value (well below the elastic limit) known as the "endurance limit" [9] in order to avoid rupture from "fatigue." With duralumin, which was formerly used for connecting rods, on account of its light weight, the endurance limit diminishes continuously as the number of load repetitions increases and consequently it has become less satisfactory as the interval before overhaul has been increased. The endurance limit for forged steel is constant for any number of load applications in excess of 10 millions; this is the material now used for connecting rods.

All airplane engines are ultimately air-cooled, some by the direct flow of air over fins or other extended surfaces on the cylinders, others by liquids which, in turn, are cooled by air flow through radiators. Neither air- nor liquid-cooled engines have demonstrated a final superiority. The liquid-

cooled type can be made more compact—with a smaller
frontal area, permitting a smaller fuselage or nacelle—but
is definitely more vulnerable since it may be made inopera-
tive by injury to any part of the liquid circulation system.
The liquid used is usually ethylene glycol with a boiling
point at 387° F. The lower temperature of a liquid-cooled
cylinder permits higher compression ratios for a given
octane value fuel. The resistance or drag of the cooling air
over the cylinders or through the radiator has been much
reduced by improved design. There is a possibility that it
may be made zero or even negative through a successful
utilization of the reactive force of the heated air as it discharges into the general atmosphere.

One of the outstanding problems with airplane engines
has been the maintenance of exhaust valves. These operate
at a dull red heat—plainly visible at night—and consequently corrode and warp. They are cooled by conduction
to the valve seat during the interval when the valve is
closed. The durability has been increased by making the
valves and their stems hollow and placing some metallic
sodium in the hollow. When operating, the sodium melts
and carries the heat bodily from the valve face to the cooler
valve stem.

Diesel Engines. The Diesel engine has had much pub-
licity as the ultimate in efficiency. This engine was started
just fifty years ago and was based on theoretical studies.
It took a long time for its realization as a practical engine.
Today it is the most economical small or medium-sized
engine in localities where oil is available at reasonable cost.
It can operate with a great variety of liquid fuels. Its most
important field is for transportation, in locomotives, marine
use, trucks, tractors, etc., and in this application it has
demonstrated great reliability and high efficiency.

It is a curious fact that alone among the various heat
engines the Diesel engine has shown no important im-

provement in thermal efficiency throughout its life. Thirty years ago it was markedly superior to all other engines in that respect, but at the present day that is not true. There is no indication of the direction to take for higher Diesel efficiencies other than the minor improvements from better design. The capacity—that is, the work done by a cylinder of given size—has been greatly increased by the use of supercharging, to which it is better adapted than the explosion engine. It has been built in sizes up to 15,000 kw. but is unduly large, heavy, and costly for such powers. It has the great advantage of absence of spark plugs and the rest of the ignition gear usual in an explosion engine.

The Combustion Turbine. The advantages which the steam turbine possesses over the steam engine have already been suggested. Engineers have long wondered whether a combustion turbine could be developed with similar advantages over the internal-combustion engine. Much work has been done on this problem, but generally with the objective of devising a turbine with an efficiency comparable with, or better than, that of an explosion engine or a Diesel engine. So far all experimental results have fallen far short of this, and the indications are that they will continue to do so. The main reasons for this are that for high efficiency the combustion turbine must operate with high temperature and with high compression ratio [10]. In the reciprocating engine, the high temperature of combustion is permissible because it occurs for only a brief time, and the containing cylinder is vigorously cooled. In an efficient turbine the process is one of steady flow; that is, the condition at any point is always constant, and consequently the combustion temperature is maintained constantly in the combustion chamber. For high efficiency the temperature of the gases at the turbine buckets must be considerably higher than can be tolerated, since the buckets are rotating at a high speed and are subjected to high centrifugal stresses. The maximum practicable temperature for turbine buckets at the present time is about 1,000° F., although recent metallurgical developments give promise of raising this by 200 or 300 degrees.

The compression, which in the reciprocating engine is carried out efficiently in the cylinder in which combustion and expansion occur, in a turbine must take place in a separate device. A reciprocating compressor cannot be considered since it would involve a cylinder as large as that of the engine which it is proposed to displace. The only compact and commercially practicable compressor is a steady-flow device such as a centrifugal compressor or, more recently, an axial-flow compressor. Centrifugal compressors are of relatively low efficiency, so that a large fraction of the work done by the turbine would have to be absorbed in driving the compressor; in many situations, it is not sufficient to do even that. Recently [11] the axial-flow compressor has been improved and can now give an efficiency of nearly 90 per cent. This disposes of one of the two obstacles to high efficiency but the temperature difficulty still remains.

The recent developments in the combustion turbine do not come primarily from improvement in materials or in compressor efficiency but from a limitation of objective. If the search for high efficiency is abandoned, a machine is available of extraordinary simplicity and compactness, low labor and maintenance costs, large power possibilities per unit, low consumption of lubricants, high rotative speed (with consequent reduction in the size and cost of a direct-connected electric generator), small size of foundations, absence of vibrations, etc. Such a unit is of great value for installations whose total operating time per year is small, such as stand-by or peak-load plants which have to be immediately available but which will be called upon only at long intervals for a short period of operation.

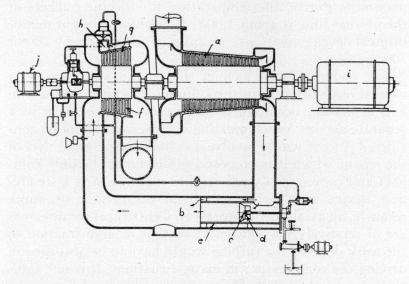

FIG. 70. Diagram of the combustion turbine.

FIG. 71. Rotor of combustion turbine.

FIG. 72. Casing for rotor of combustion turbine.

The combustion turbine now available has the advantages mentioned but only one-half the efficiency of the Diesel engine. It consists, as shown in Figure 70, of a multi-stage, axial-flow compressor on the same shaft as a com-

FIG. 73. Assembly of the combustion turbine.

bustion turbine [12]. Air is compressed to an absolute pressure of about 4 atmospheres, is heated to a temperature of 1,000° F. by fuel burned in the air stream, and then goes to the turbine. The machine is subjected to low pressure only, and to a tolerable temperature. Some other source of power, such as a small Diesel engine, is required to start it. No water is needed and no lubrication except at the main bearings. The excess of the power produced by the turbine over that required to drive the compressor is absorbed by an electric generator on the common shaft. The efficiency under test is about 16 per cent.

This machine is in use as an emergency power plant located in a bomb-proof shelter and for other purposes. It has been proposed and may be in operation in the German Navy for the main power plant of destroyers. A destroyer runs normally at a low cruising speed, for which power may be supplied by relatively small Diesel engines, and it must be prepared to develop large power on occasion. This can be accomplished by the combustion turbine in a very small fraction of the time required by the usual steam-turbine plant. The economy would be about the same as that of the steam turbine. The absence of boilers and condensing equipment reduces the vulnerability of the plant. The reduction in the operating personnel would be considerable.

Another application under consideration is for use in locomotives. Steam locomotives have thermal efficiencies which range usually from 5 to 8 per cent. Compared with these the efficiency of the combustion turbine is good, but it is considerably less than that of the Diesel locomotive. Its justification for locomotive use, as compared with the Diesel engine, comes from low weight, greater compactness (so that 5,000 hp. can go in a single car), the absence of reciprocating parts (with resulting improvement in balance and reduction in track maintenance), absence of water supply and of the water-cooling radiator, and lower cost. There are still some problems to be worked out, particularly with reference to operation at partial loads, but the future looks quite promising.

STEADY-FLOW PROCESSES

The preceding discussion illustrates the definite trend in engineering practice in recent years toward the substitution of steady-flow processes for discontinuous procedures, a trend which covers compressors and pumps as well as power generators. The earlier power generators were all steady-flow devices, that is, the working substance flowed through them continuously. Water wheels and windmills have always been of this character, as also was the reaction steam turbine imagined by Hero of Alexandria around two thousand years ago. With the advent of the steam engine about two hundred years ago the cylinder and piston were introduced and this entails a reciprocating motion, the alternate admission and rejection of the working fluid, and discontinuous action. This development resulted necessarily from the lack of knowledge at that time of fluid mechanics, but even had that knowledge been available then, the condition of the mechanic arts was such that machinery could not have been built which would function at the necessary speeds if acceptable efficiencies were to be obtained. It was not until near the end of the last century that theory and the mechanic arts were developed sufficiently to permit the fabrication of steam-power units operating with good efficiency under steady-flow conditions. In the case of the internal combustion engine, there has been and is still the additional difficulty of finding materials which retain adequate strength at the high temperatures necessary for high efficiency.

The steady-flow process employs curved surfaces across which the fluid—steam, air, water, etc.—flows and which are deflected by such flow. (Reaction machines in which the fluid undergoes a pressure drop are not included in this discussion.) If the fluid is stationary and the curved surface rotates, a pressure is exerted on that surface which, in air, may be the thrust that propels an airplane or, in water, that which propels a ship; if the surface does not rotate, the pressure may support a structure as in the lift of the wings of an airplane.

If the rotating curved surfaces cannot advance, the pressure exerted by them on the fluid will give velocity to that fluid as in fans, compressors, and pumps.

If the fluid is moving and comes in contact with rotatable blades, it may do work on them as in windmills, water wheels, steam turbines, etc.

The curved surfaces must be designed for particular operating conditions. If these conditions change, the efficiency of the performance of the unit diminishes. The simplest practical way of decreasing such loss of efficiency is to change the angle at which the curved surface is inclined to the direction of motion or, as it is commonly described, to alter the pitch. Other procedures, such as warping the curved surface, are possible but in general are not practicable. The desirability of changing the pitch varies greatly with different types of apparatus. For a marine propeller it is comparatively unimportant but for an air propeller which operates in a medium whose density changes with altered altitude and which rotates at constant rpm., variable pitch is most important. As has been indicated, variable pitch is desirable for windmills and water wheels. For steam turbines the blades are so numerous that variable pitch becomes impracticable—fortunately it is not very important for this application.

Summing up, it may be said that the chief recent advances have been in the substitution of steady-flow processes for intermittent procedures and in the application of variable pitch devices in those steady-flow machines which are most benefited by it.

For References see p. 300.

VII

SOME FUNDAMENTAL ASPECTS OF PHOTOSYNTHESIS

By JAMES FRANCK

University of Chicago

IT is generally known to scientists that photosynthesis is the synthesis of organic matter in green plants with the help of the sunlight, and that this process is the only source of organic matter existing on earth. However, this simple statement contains many premises taken from the field of physical chemistry which must be discussed.

Organic matter consists of carbon, hydrogen, some oxygen, and often additional elements in smaller proportions. To answer the question of why organic matter is not formed on the earth without photosynthesis it is necessary to explain why it cannot be formed through the agency of heat energy alone. The atmosphere of the earth was exceedingly hot when our planet was being formed, and at such high temperatures most chemical compounds cannot exist but rather are dissociated into free atoms. Slowly the earth cooled and the compounds were formed which are found, for instance, in the solid crust of the earth. Organic matter was, of course, also formed at that time as an intermediate product. But since all organic matter is oxidized in the presence of oxygen, and heat is liberated in the course of this reaction, we conclude that at high temperatures organic matter is not a stable configuration of carbon, hydrogen, and oxygen. The organic matter formed at high temperatures will, therefore, be short-lived and will combine with oxygen to form stable products, such as carbon dioxide and water.

The geologist and mineralogist have thus come to the conclusion not only that organic matter was absent as the crust of the earth was slowly formed, but also that oxygen was practically absent from the atmosphere. The conditions which prevail now, wherein our atmosphere contains about 20 per cent oxygen, are, like the production of organic matter, the result of photosynthesis.

The next question which arises is why organic matter, once it has been produced under the influence of light, is stable enough to make life possible at the low temperatures now prevailing on earth. Why, for instance, does not the organic matter of which our bodies consist immediately react with oxygen to form carbon dioxide and water? A similar question arises also in the case of inorganic substances. For instance, we know that a mixture of illuminating gas and oxygen can be prepared which is entirely inert at low temperatures. To start the oxidation one has to initiate the reaction by heating a small part of the gas or igniting it with a match, a spark, or similar device. Why does the reaction have to be initiated? The answer is that the molecules have to come very close together before the reaction can begin; they do not come very close together if they collide with one another at low temperatures because the velocities are small and at close range the molecules repel each other. The exact nature of these repelling forces is now explained by modern quantum theory. By raising the temperature the force of the impacts is increased, since the kinetic energy of the atoms and molecules rises proportionately to the absolute temperature. The greater the relative kinetic energy of the colliding particles, the more they can penetrate into the mutual spheres of repulsion, and the nearer the centers of gravity will approach each other; thus, the reaction will start. In the case of reactions which release energy, like the burning of illuminating gas, the energy liberated will raise the temperature of the surrounding gas and therefore activate it; thus, the reactions will spread throughout all the gas present. One uses the term "heat of activation" to describe the phenomenon discussed. The term "potential barrier" or "potential wall" is also used in analogy to mechanical processes.

Figure 74 may represent a mountain, and a stone brought close to the top is said to possess potential energy which will go over into

FIG. 74. A "potential barrier" prevents the stone from falling down the hill.

kinetic energy and, eventually, into heat as the stone rolls down the mountain to the lowest point. If a little wall is built on the slope of the mountain at the point where we deposited the stone, then some energy will be required to lift the stone to the top of the wall before it can fall down. Just so it is necessary to put in some energy to overcome the initial starting resistance of the chemical reaction. There are reactions with a great heat of activation—a high potential wall—and reactions with small ones.

Following the mechanical analogy, one can use energy diagrams. In Figure 75 the lower level on the right side may represent a stable modification of a chemical compound, the higher level to the left an unstable one. We may, in this instance, let the higher level represent organic matter plus oxygen, and the lower level represent carbon dioxide plus water. The transition from the higher level to the lower level can proceed only over the top of the potential barrier; and, since the particles do not possess enough kinetic energy at low temperature to overcome this barrier, the reaction will not start and the organic matter will be stable in the

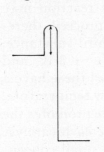

FIG. 75. A potential barrier prevents an unstable compound from going over to a more stable form.

presence of oxygen. However, this principle alone is not enough to explain why life is possible, because we know that food is burned in the human or animal body to develop the energy necessary for the processes of life and it has to be done at the low temperatures prevailing, for instance, in the human body. All these oxidation reactions are accomplished with the help of catalysts which, when associated with life processes, are known under the name of enzymes. Many vitamins belong to this group. A catalyst is a chemical substance which, when added in small concentrations to the reaction mixture, activates the reaction without being used up itself. A catalyst may enter into a chemical reaction itself, but it is finally restored unchanged by a second chemical reaction. By its presence, therefore, instead of a reaction which has a high heat of activation, two or more partial reactions occur, each of which has a small heat of activation and can, therefore, proceed at lower temperature as illustrated in Figure 76.

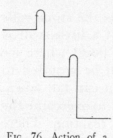

FIG. 76. Action of a catalyst.

Let us take a simple example. Suppose a molecule A_2 to react with molecule B_2 to form $2AB$. This reaction may have a great heat of activation and may not proceed, therefore, at room temperature. However, if a third substance, C_2, is added the partial reactions $A_2 + C_2 \rightarrow 2AC$ and $2AC + B_2 \rightarrow 2AB + C_2$ may occur. If both of these have a small heat of activation, they can occur at low temperature. In that case C_2 acts as a catalyst. Its presence promotes the reaction without the destruction of C_2. Since each catalyst molecule can be used over and over again a small concentration of catalyst molecules is all that is needed. The total reaction will proceed just as fast as the catalyst molecules go through their own reaction cycle.

This discussion may be sufficient to give an understanding of why organic matter can serve as food and be slowly oxidized at the low temperature prevailing in the animal body. Indeed, there are many catalysts connected with the oxidation process in living tissue, and each reaction step develops so small an amount of energy that the other surrounding molecules are not activated—contrary to the behavior in the burning of illuminating gas mentioned above.

Next, we should discuss why light energy alone is especially suited to reverse the process of burning in producing organic matter and oxygen by the combination of carbon dioxide and water. It has been mentioned that the use of heat energy is unfavorable because the organic matter, once made, will be burned up again. But when visible light is absorbed by a cold gas, the individual molecules take up one quantum of energy at a time, an amount which is several hundred times larger than the energy of thermal motion. This energy can be used to reduce CO_2 and H_2O, producing organic matter. Furthermore, the freshly formed products remaining in the environment do not burn up because the temperature is too low. The energy amounts given by absorption-acts to the individual molecules depend upon the color of the light. With red light the energy is about 100 times as great as that due to temperature movement at room temperature. With blue it is nearly 200 times as large; and with ultraviolet it is even larger. In accordance with the quantum theory, light is emitted and absorbed in energy units, the magnitude of which is proportional to the frequency of the light and, therefore, indirectly proportional to the wave lengths.

It will not be possible to discuss here all the experimental proofs for the quantum theory. I shall, therefore, confine myself to the one which follows immediately out of photochemical observations as Einstein [1] showed in the year 1912 by establishing his fundamental law of photochemical equivalence. Light energy can be used for photochemical reactions only if it is absorbed; if the absorption of light takes place in quanta, the number of molecules which are activated by the light to undergo chemical reactions must be equal to the number of quanta absorbed by these molecules. If this consequence of the quantum theory is correct, we can predict what is to be expected for such simple photochemical reactions as photodissociation of diatomic molecules. The behavior of iodine may be taken as an example, since iodine is a gas which absorbs light throughout virtually the whole visible spectrum. Moreover, from many thermochemical experiments, the exact amount of energy necessary to dissociate an iodine molecule into two iodine atoms is known. Let us irradiate a bulb containing iodine vapor with monochromatic light and change the wave lengths from the direction of the long wave-length region, red and infrared, to the short wave-length region, blue and ultraviolet. No dissociation processes will take place by irradiation in the long wave-length region, regardless of the intensity of the light. But on going over to shorter wave lengths, we certainly shall have the occurrence of dissociation processes at the very moment when the size of the quantum absorbed becomes equal to the heat of dissociation of the iodine molecule. It can be shown that, in this case, all the energy will be used for the dissociation processes. The gas will not become warmer if the recombination of the atoms is hindered. As further progress is made into the short wave-length region, the quanta become larger than the heat of dissociation—only a part of the energy may be used for the dissociation process, the rest being dissipated into the temperature

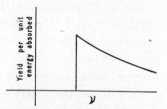

Fig. 77. Curve showing the variation in the number of molecules photolyzed per unit of radiant energy absorbed, as a function of the wave length.

movement. The use of energy for the dissociation process plotted as a function of the frequency will then show a curve like that of Figure 77; the yield will be zero until the critical threshold is reached; at the threshold the maximum yield will be obtained, and from then on the yield per unit of energy absorbed will fall slowly. This is actually the behavior observed in many photochemical reactions.

In applying the basic laws of photochemistry to the processes of photosynthesis, we have to consider the fact that only visible light is available for this process. In the infrared the quanta are too small to be of any value for the production of organic matter, while the ultraviolet emitted by the sun will not reach the surface of the earth because it is absorbed in the higher levels of our atmosphere by the ozone formed photochemically in these layers out of oxygen. But visible light is not absorbed by either carbon dioxide or by water, since neither shows any color. To reduce carbon dioxide photochemically a dyestuff is needed which absorbs the visible light and transfers the energy to the carbon dioxide and water. Reactions of this type are called sensitized photochemical processes. The essential dyestuff is a plant pigment, known as chlorophyll, which, as its name indicates, is responsible for the green color of leaves and other plants. As will be shown more clearly later on, chlorophyll is itself a complicated organic molecule; and we are therefore confronted with the following difficulty: Photosynthesis is the only source of organic matter on earth. On the other hand, photosynthesis itself requires the presence of a dyestuff which, in turn, belongs to the class of organic molecules. Under these circumstances, how could the process of photosynthesis ever have started? The answer is, that photosynthesis, as it is known today, had a predecessor which produced organic matter without the help of a dyestuff. This proto-photosynthesis must have occurred when no oxygen was present in the atmosphere and, consequently, the ozone layer was also absent. At that time ultraviolet light could reach the surface of the earth, and the absorption of it by carbon dioxide as well as by water molecules could take place directly so that the help of the dyestuff was not needed. The organic matter formed in this way might again have been partly destroyed by ultraviolet light, were it not for the fact that the substances, once formed, would be taken up by the water and protected from destruction. This condition is probably the physical basis for the biologist's opinion that life started in the water.

Returning now to the process of photosynthesis in plants, it will be necessary to consider how the process is quantitatively measured. To do this, we write down in a simple chemical equation that which we said before in words.

$$6CO_2 + 6H_2O + E \rightarrow (CH_2O)_6 + 6O_2 \qquad (1)$$

Thus we have in this equation the assumption that a sugar hexose was made by photosynthesis, which requires reduction of 6 carbon dioxide molecules. It is not essential that the photochemical end-product be hexose itself, but it is essential that the product have an oxidation state of a sugar like hexose [2]. It can then be calculated from the heat of the combustion (E) of such a sugar how much energy is necessary to reduce 1 carbon dioxide molecule, and we find that the energy is several times greater than the energy transmitted by one visible light quantum to the dyestuff, chlorophyll. The uptake of carbon dioxide and the evolution of oxygen can be followed manometrically, with the aid of the so-called Warburg manometer (compare Fig. 78). This method makes use of the difference between the solubility of carbon dioxide and of oxygen in water. Unicellular water plants such as algae are used, for the most part, in such experiments. The plants are suspended in water which may fill half of the vessel seen in Figure 78 at the right side of the manometer to which it is connected. A beam of light passing through the bottom of this vessel illuminates the plants. The gas phase contains air and an admixture of carbon dioxide. If the carbon dioxide molecules are taken up and oxygen is evolved, the pressure will rise, since oxygen is much less soluble in water than carbon dioxide. Among the other methods of measuring photosynthesis, we may describe the spectroscopic one, wherein the amount of carbon dioxide present in the gas atmosphere is measured by its absorption coefficient for infrared light of wave length 4 μ.

In the device developed by McAlister [3], the gas is circulated in a closed system containing a plant chamber in which a plant is irradiated with white light and another partition in which the content of CO_2 in the gas atmosphere is measured spectroscopically. As photosynthesis proceeds, the amount of CO_2 becomes smaller and, correspondingly, the intensity of the 4 μ radiation, which penetrates the absorption chamber, increases. Curves in which this intensity is plotted as function of time are easily transferred in rate curves of photosynthesis.

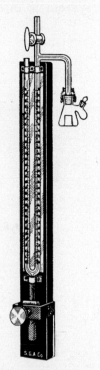

FIG. 78. Warburg manometer as described on page 186.

Before discussing the results of such measurements I should like to mention reasons why the dyestuff, chlorophyll, is especially fitted to sensitize photosynthesis. Figure 79 shows the chemical structure of chlorophyll as now established. Although it is not our task to discuss chlorophyll structure in detail, it may be emphasized that the system of conjugated double bonds, which extends throughout the whole structure, is responsible for the color. The term

"conjugated double bonds" means that single bonds between carbon atoms alternate with double bonds. If that
system is interrupted by either oxidation or reduction of

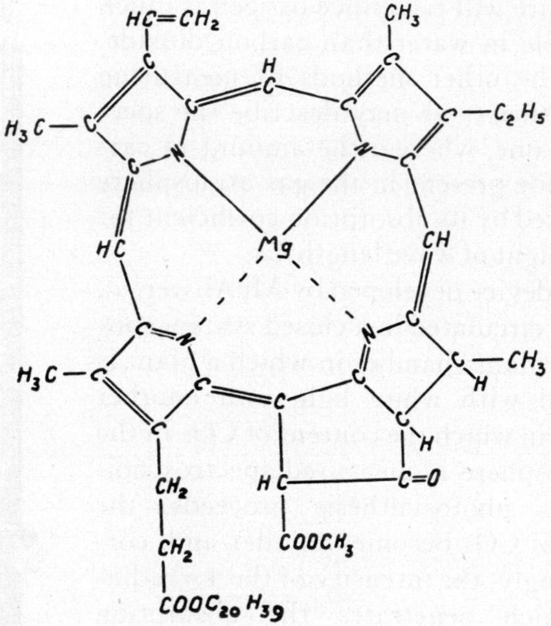

FIG. 79. Chemical structure of chlorophyll

one of the carbon atoms which belongs to the system of conjugated bonds, the color will vanish, producing the so-called
leucodye. In the past this fact has been used as evidence
that chlorophyll itself cannot enter the chemical reactions
of photosynthesis and undergo periodic oxidation and reduction, since the chlorophyll in a photosynthesizing plant
is not bleached at all. But the chlorophyll also has groups of
atoms that are not connected with the system of conjugated
bonds. Oxidation or reduction in these groups will not
influence the color. Indeed, there are reasons which make

it probable that chlorophyll not only acts as a sensitizer but also does enter into the course of the reaction [4]. But even if it should be demonstrated that chlorophyll is not specific in its chemical reaction, it undoubtedly is specific for photosynthesis by virtue of its physical properties. First, it belongs to the class of fluorescent dyestuffs. The ability of these molecules to fluoresce is always associated with the ability to induce photochemical reactions [5]. Fluorescence means that a part of the light absorbed is quickly reëmitted with or without change of color. This phenomenon is, I suppose, generally well known. I may remind you of the fluorescence of fluorescein solutions.

Of course, light reëmitted as fluorescence is lost for the purposes of photochemistry and, conversely, if most of the light is used for photochemical processes, fluorescence should be weak. Nevertheless, the fact that a dyestuff is able to fluoresce is important for the photochemical action, since it offers a proof that the energy absorbed remains for awhile as a unit in the molecule and is not dissipated immediately into the degrees of freedom associated with heat movement. Actually, the time during which the energy remains together in the molecule can be calculated from the strength of absorption and the amount of light reëmitted. In the case of chlorophyll, under the conditions prevailing in a plant, the energy stays together for a very short time $(10^{-10}$ seconds) [6] although even this time is long compared to the time of normal kinetic gas collisions. Due to the fact that the energy is not immediately dissipated, conditions are favorable for it to be transferred to the carbon dioxide and water molecules. In order for this transfer to become effective, the atoms must all be located favorably with respect to each other. Since the molecules rotate and oscillate, it may take some time before the right steric configuration is reached. If the energy did not stay together, the right geometric arrangement would have to be present at the very moment of absorption. Inasmuch as this is highly improbable, the photochemical yield is small if non-fluorescing dyes are used as sensitizers. But the ability to fluoresce is shared by chlorophyll with many other dye-stuffs. The specificity of the chlorophyll is seen in the fact

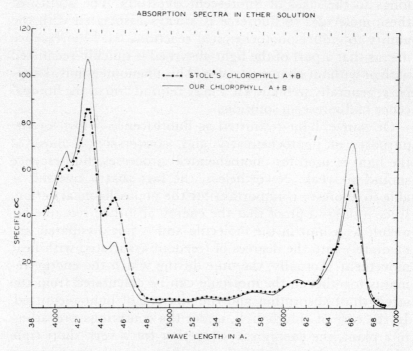

ABSORPTION SPECTRA IN ETHER SOLUTION

Fig. 80. Absorption spectrum of chlorophyll, after Zscheile [7].

that it retains only a given amount of energy from the light quanta absorbed, regardless of the color of the light absorbed; the remainder is immediately transferred into heat. This consequence can be drawn from the observation that the fluorescent light always has the same red color regardless of whether the chlorophyll is irradiated with red, blue, or ultraviolet light. The energy corresponding to a quantum of red light is the amount retained in the chlorophyll and usable in the process of photosynthesis. In this way the amount of energy used for the photochemical process is always the same, regardless of the wave lengths of the light absorbed by the chlorophyll. Otherwise, one would expect that the blue light, which has quanta that are almost twice as great as the quanta of red light, would induce quite different reactions from those of the quanta of the longer wave lengths.

As Figure 80 shows, the absorption is strong in the red and in the blue, whereas in the green region of the spectrum the absorption coefficient is small but still not zero, so that light of all wave lengths, throughout the visible region, can be used for the process of photosynthesis. Quantitative measurements of the oxygen evolution or the carbon dioxide uptake and of the energy of the light absorbed make it possible to calculate the number of absorption acts necessary for the reduction of a single carbon dioxide molecule. The value E of the chemical equation (1) allows us to predict that at least four absorption acts would be necessary, since the energy of a quantum of red light is less than one-third the heat of combustion. But the fact that several absorption acts are necessary leads to the conclusion that the energy absorbed in the form of light energy has to be greater than the amount (E) of equation (1). Each absorption act has to produce an intermediate product of photosynthesis (a partially reduced molecule of carbon dioxide), and the intermediates have to be so stable that they can wait until the next absorption act transforms the product one step further.

Extra amounts of energy are then needed for potential barriers which prevent the freshly formed photoproducts from falling back stepwise in an exceedingly short time to the lowest energy state which belongs to the products' carbon dioxide and water. The energy diagram of Figure 81, which is analogous to the one used in Figure 76, may elucidate this fact. The difference in height between the ground state and the highest one corresponds to the energy amount (E), but the total energy needed to reach the highest level starting at the ground state surpasses (E) by an amount equal to the sum of all the potential barriers of the intermediates. To get the necessary stability, the height of the potential barriers has to be so great that it is very unlikely that only 4

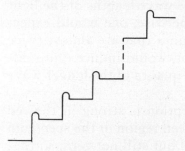

Fig. 81. Energy levels of the intermediate products of photosynthesis.

quanta would be necessary to reduce a carbon dioxide molecule, as the earlier measurements of Warburg [8] seemed to indicate. Recent measurements [9] [10] [11], made in several laboratories, show that 10 to 12 quanta are used up in the reduction of 1 carbon dioxide molecule. Taking into account the fact that some energy losses may occur, for instance, by inefficiency of the chlorophyll, one certainly has the right to conclude that at least 8 photochemical steps are necessary and, correspondingly, there will exist at least 7 intermediate products between the stage represented by carbon dioxide and water and that of carbohydrate and free oxygen.

The research discussed so far seems to show that photosynthesis is a complicated, sensitized, photochemical process taking place in successive stages, but it reveals nothing which principally would distinguish photosynthesis in any way from other photochemical processes. However, new assumptions have to be introduced the moment we wish to understand the shape of the curve obtained when the rate of photosynthesis is plotted against light intensity. As shown in Figure 82, photosynthesis at low light intensities is proportional to the strength of the incident light; at medium intensities it rises less rapidly; and at high light intensities becomes independent of further increases in

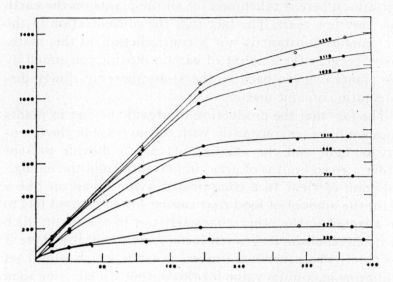

FIG. 82. Rate of photosynthesis as a function of light intensity at various CO_2 concentrations (Hoover, Johnston, and Brackett [12]).

light intensity. In other words, one gets a saturation curve. The rate of photosynthesis at saturation depends upon the amount of carbon dioxide present, but this is true only until a certain minimum concentration of carbon dioxide is reached, which corresponds to a few tenths of 1 per cent of this gas. A further increase of the concentration of carbon dioxide does not change the situation further; in other words, carbon dioxide ceases to be limiting at these concentrations.

Photosynthesis is very efficient in the use of the carbon dioxide present in our atmosphere. In normal air the concentration of carbon dioxide is only 0.04 per cent. At this low concentration the saturation rate is only slightly lower than the maximum rate of photosynthesis occurring in the presence of a surplus of CO_2. Indeed, photosynthesis is so efficient that the total amount of carbon dioxide present in our atmosphere is consumed by all the plants on the earth in a very few years. The fact that the concentration in the air remains constant is not a contradiction to this statement, because the amount of carbon dioxide consumed by the plants is given back to the atmosphere by slowly disintegrating organic matter.

The fact that the production of organic matter in plants does not increase constantly with the increase in the intensity of light and the amount of carbon dioxide present above a given limit is of great importance from the biological point of view. In a complicated living organism like a plant the amount of food that can be stored or used has to be adapted to the other characteristics of the plant, such as its metabolism, its growth factor, and so on. But there is no purely photochemical process possible which would set a limiting maximum value for this output. In fact, one soon realizes that the occurrence of this limit can only be explained by the assumption that photosynthesis is a process in which not only photochemical processes but also nonphotochemical reactions must occur. A total reaction will not proceed more rapidly than its slowest partial reaction, just as a marching troop will travel no faster than the slowest soldier in the group. The velocity of the photochemical partial reactions will, of course, rise proportionately to the intensity of the incident light, but the thermochemical partial reactions necessary to complete photosynthesis are not influenced by light; and one of them will, therefore, at a sufficiently high light intensity, become the slowest partial reaction. At saturation the limited velocity of the slowest dark reaction is alone responsible for the limitation of the output. With this assumption it is possible to calculate from the shape of the saturation curve the velocity with which the dark reaction has to proceed.

Simple mathematical equations show that at an output corresponding to half the saturation value the velocity of the slowest dark reaction is equal to that of the overall photochemical reaction. This last can be calculated from the quantum yield, the number of chlorophyll molecules present, etc. One gets the result that the slowest dark reaction should run half way to completion in about a minute. On the other hand, it is possible to measure directly the velocity of the dark reaction and to compare this result with the theoretical one. The best measurements of this kind were made by Emerson and Arnold [13], who used the method of flash illumination. They illuminated plants with

brief light flashes and varied the time intervals between the flashes. In Figure 83 the time is plotted as the abscissa and the intensity of the light as the ordinate. Each light flash, then, corresponds to a very narrow column in this figure, while the dark pauses between the flashes

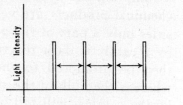

Fig. 83. Flashing-light illumination [10].

are represented by the distances between these columns. If a light flash produces a given amount of photochemical products, the next light flash will find the photochemical apparatus in the same state as did the first, provided the time interval between the flashes is long enough for the dark reaction to run through to its completion. If, on the other hand, the time interval is too short, the subsequent light flashes will find material still accumulated from the previous light flashes, and the yield per flash will, therefore, be smaller than would otherwise be the case. Emerson and Arnold measured the yield per flash as a function of the dark time and, in that way, observed directly the time taken by the slowest dark reaction to run to completion. The result was an unexpected one: the time needed was only about $\frac{1}{100}$ of a second instead of 60 seconds. The observation differed from the expectation by a factor of about 6,000. Many attempts were made to overcome this difficulty, but in the present discussion it will be possible to mention only the explanation which we have reason to believe is the correct one [14].

Calculation of the velocity of the dark reaction is tacitly based on the assumption that all material produced photochemically must undergo a chemical change in the dark before the next photochemical step can proceed. But this assumption is not necessary. One can substitute for this assumption the hypothesis that the freshly formed photochemical products are very unstable; at high light intensities only a part of the products will then be transformed by a catalytic dark reaction to a new product, which will then be promoted to the next reduction state by light, whereas the bulk of the substance not immediately caught by the catalyst will fall back to the old oxidation state on account of the instability of the newly formed photochemical product which has not undergone the catalytic reaction. Figure 84 illustrates the assumption. The light quanta may transform the CO_2 molecule into one with a lower oxidation state, which is protected against back reactions by a very small potential barrier. The lifetime of this freshly formed product is short: not longer than about a thousandth of a second. From the level of the unstable photochemical product a narrow passageway leads down to a much more stable level: that of the catalytically transformed intermediate product. The bottleneck, which allows only a certain amount of material to go through the passage, is due to the presence of only a limited amount of the catalyst (designated by the letter B in the figure) which transforms the unstable product into the more stable one. The molecules of catalyst B present can handle only a given amount of material, since it takes some time for each catalyst molecule to go through the reaction cycle. All of the photoproduct that the catalyst B cannot handle will not accumulate in the unstable state, but will fall down in the lower state, as indicated by the arrows. It is necessary to assume that catalyst B has to act on each photochemical intermediate product of photosynthesis; in other words, all the freshly formed photoproducts are supposed to be unstable and have to be stabilized by a catalytic reaction involving B. This follows from the fact that, under normal

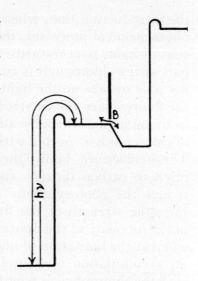

FIG. 84. Schematic representation to show that only a little of the material raised to the higher energy level can get through the narrow passageway (by means of catalyst B) and so reach a more stable configuration. The rest falls back again to the original low energy value.

conditions, the relative concentrations of the intermediates are the same at saturation and at low light intensities. Otherwise one would obtain a temporary anomalous rate in weak light immediately after an exposure to a strong irradiation. The time measured in Emerson and Arnold's experiments is, then, the time necessary for a catalyst B molecule to go through a reaction cycle, and the maximum yield per light flash is the measure of the number of catalyst molecules present. This hypothesis explains satisfactorily the occurrence of the saturation and the result of the flash experiments mentioned.

The foregoing hypothesis can be tested by experiments on fluorescence of green plants [15] [16]. It was mentioned in the introduction that, when most of the energy is used for photochemical processes, the fluorescence, i.e., the reëmission of light, is necessarily weak. If, on the other hand, a part of the chlorophyll is connected with material which is not able to take up the light energy for chemical processes, the fluorescence will be stronger. Indeed, this can be shown in living plants when, by addition of narcotics, the surface of chlorophyll is covered with photoinsensitive material [17]. These substances hinder the flow of energy from the chlorophyll to carbon dioxide and intermediates and therefore reduce the photosynthetic output and at the same time raise the strength of the fluorescent light. Measurements of the intensity of the fluorescence will, consequently, show whether the limitation of photosynthesis is accompanied by an accumulation of photoinsensitive material in contact with the chlorophyll or whether the limitation occurs in such a way that no accumulation of photoinsensitive material takes place.

It is clear that the hypothesis put forward above emphasizes the statement that no photoinsensitive material will be accumulated, since it is assumed that the saturation is caused by the limitation of a catalytic reaction acting on a chemically unstable product. The product formed by the aid of catalyst B is photosensitive, as is the substance resulting from the rapid back reactions. The concentration of the unstable photoproduct, which may be photoinsensitive, always remains exceedingly small. Indeed, measurements of fluorescence show that the fluorescence intensity rises in a linear ratio with light intensity in an intensity region that is already producing saturation of photosynthesis [17]. If normal saturation were associated with an accumulation of photoinsensitive material, the fluorescence should rise faster than linearly in the intensity region where the photosynthesis curve shows the transition to saturation.

The dark reaction involving catalyst B is not the only

one associated with photosynthesis. This can again be shown by experiments on saturation in continuous and flashing light [18], by fluorescence experiments, and by important results gained by Kamen, Ruben, and coworkers [19] who used the method of labeled carbon atoms.

The saturation rate of photosynthesis is very sensitive to cyanide. The question arises whether cyanide poisons cata-

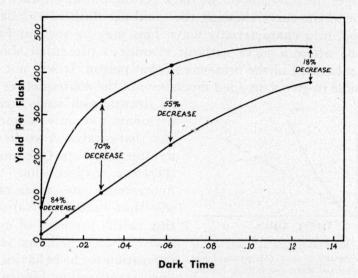

FIG. 85. Illustrating coöperation of catalysts B and A as explained on p. 200. (S. Weller and J. Franck [18].)

lyst B or whether some other catalyst, which is present in a surplus under normal conditions and so has no effect on the saturation rate, is so much reduced in its activity by that poison that it becomes limiting [18]. If the number of active B molecules would be reduced by cyanide, the maximal photosynthetic gas exchange obtainable by single light flashes should also be reduced. Actually this yield remains unaltered by the addition of HCN. But the duration of the dark periods between two consecutive flashes necessary to attain this maximum yield per flash becomes prolonged by the addition of the poison. Just this behavior is to be expected if the dark period is, in the presence of cyanide, not only a measure of the time needed by catalyst B to go through its reaction cycle, but is also influenced by the limitations of a second catalytic reaction.

The coöperation of the two catalysts, B and A, not only changes the duration of the dark period, but also alters the shape of the curve showing the yield per flash *versus* dark period, in a characteristic way. This may be seen in Figure 85 where a curve without cyanide is presented above one measured in the presence of that poison. It will not be possible to give a detailed discussion of the consequences to be drawn from such measurements but only to mention that catalyst A works on a stable substrate. One must, therefore, expect that the fluorescence rises more rapidly than linearly as saturation in the presence of cyanide is approached, that is in opposition to the behavior at normal saturation. Figure 86 shows that the fluorescence plotted as the function of light intensity shows the expected deviation from linearity.* It was also possible to discover the function of catalyst A. According to the work of Kamen and Ruben [19], who made use of the radioactive tracer technique, carbon dioxide reacts in the dark with an acceptor molecule. This reaction is assisted by a catalyst sensitive toward cyanide. The compound formed by the accep-

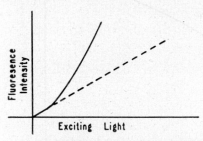

FIG. 86. Fluorescence as a function of light intensity in a cyanide-poisoned leaf (Wassink and Katz, and Franck, French, and Puck [16] [17]).

* A deviation from linearity occurs also without cyanide and in the presence of enough CO_2, but in this case only at very high light intensities and in some plants at intensities much greater than is required to obtain saturation. This effect is produced by a secondary process not to be discussed here [16].

tor molecule and carbon dioxide constitutes the photosensitive substrate. Lack of CO_2 has the same influence on the saturation and fluorescence curves as does cyanide in the

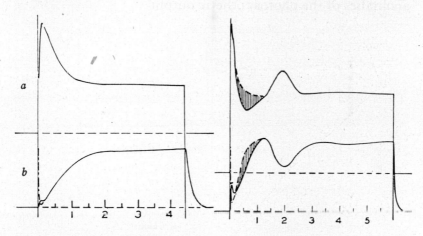

FIG. 87. Course of fluorescence (a), [15] [16] [17] [20] in comparison to the time course of photosynthesis (b).

FIG. 88. Fluorescence and photosynthetic output [15].

presence of a surplus of CO_2 [16]. In both instances the amount of substrate which undergoes the photochemical reduction process is deficient.

We must mention a third catalyst, the influence of which on the rate of photosynthesis can only be observed at the beginning of an illumination period. Again it is a catalyst that acts on a substrate stable enough to be accumulated if the catalyst (called catalyst C) is limiting. The time course of the rate of photosynthesis and of the fluorescence intensity consequently run antiparallel (work of McAlister and Myers). A few examples may show this. Curve a of Figure 87 shows the time course of the fluorescence in a higher plant, to be compared with curve b, the time course of the rate [21]. There is a strong maximum of the fluorescence after 1 second of illumination, to which corresponds the deep minimum of the photosynthetic rate. Figure 88 shows a more complicated set of curves, shown here to prove that each fluctuation of fluorescence is mirrored in the anomalies of the photosynthetic output.

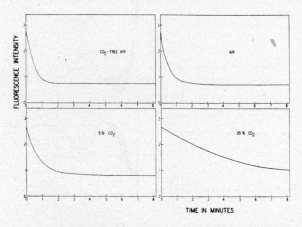

FIG. 89. Effect of CO_2 in prolonging the time of the fluorescence decay [16].

Figure 89 shows that the duration of the fluorescence outburst is prolonged by an excess of CO_2 (the same is true for the induction period of photosynthesis); with 20 per cent CO_2 it lasts, for instance, about 20 minutes, compared with about 1 minute in normal air. This fact can be used for a demonstration of the velocity with which a gas exchange takes place in a leaf [16]. To do this, the surface of a leaf, provided with an atmosphere containing a small amount of carbon dioxide, is exposed to a strong illumination so that the fluorescence outburst fades away in about a minute. A small portion of the leaf, however, is connected to a rubber tube through which gas containing a high concentration of carbon dioxide can be admitted. This part of the leaf will then be exposed to an excess of carbon dioxide, and the fluorescence will, therefore, remain strong for several minutes in that part of the leaf. At 1 minute after the beginning of irradiation the part of the leaf containing the excess of carbon dioxide fluoresces much more strongly than the other parts of the leaf. The spot which is brighter than the surroundings is not confined to the part directly

Fig. 90. Fluorescence photograph to illustrate diffusion of carbon dioxide through leaf.

connected with the rubber tube, since the carbon dioxide diffuses from this spot to other parts of the leaf. One can thus actually photograph this diffusion of the carbon dioxide through the leaf with the fluorescent method as shown in Figure 90.

It will not be possible to discuss the details of the anomalies shown in Figures 87 and 88, but I may state that they are readily understandable. The function of catalyst C is to split off oxygen from the peroxides formed as one of the photochemical end-products of photosynthesis. The concentration of catalyst C molecules is sufficient to prevent any limitation of the rate of the reaction in which it is involved

FIG. 91. Illustrating the effect of deactivation of the catalyst C as described on p. 205.

if all the molecules are in an active form. But the ratio between the number of active molecules of catalyst C and its inactive fraction depends upon the rate of photosynthesis. Catalyst C is slowly deactivated (apparently) by an oxidation process and reactivated by a reaction with the carbohydrates. Whenever the rate of photosynthesis is suddenly increased, there is a transition period during which C is limiting until enough molecules are activated. The anomalies mentioned are a direct consequence of this temporary insufficiency of the peroxide-splitting catalyst. The induction period can become of great importance for the total growth of the plant provided the plant is periodically illuminated and darkened. The deactivation of the catalyst C in the dark takes about a minute and the reactivation about the same time. The plant is, therefore, practically prevented from growing if the periods of light and dark are approximately a minute in duration as illustrated in Figure 91 [22]. The connection of this phenomenon with the induction period was first recognized by McAlister [3].

Figure 92 summarizes in an energy diagram the results of the coöperation between photochemical reactions and catalytic dark reactions. The reactions must proceed with the help of photochemical steps from the low level of the carbon dioxide and water to the level of the carbohydrates and free oxygen. The first step is an exothermic reaction between carbon dioxide and the acceptor molecule, which takes place with the help of the catalyst A. That this reaction has limited capacity is indicated by the narrow opening between the level of carbon dioxide and free acceptor molecules and the level of the carboxylated product. From this lowest level on, light quanta will raise the molecules in successive steps to the highest level, which corresponds to that of carbohydrates and peroxides. After each photochemical step, there is a narrow gateway leading from the unstable photochemical products to the stable ones. The unstable ones are protected only by a small potential barrier, so that all the material that cannot pass quickly enough through the bottleneck formed by the catalytic reaction involving catalyst B will undergo back reactions. At the highest level there is again a catalytic reaction, which serves to split off the oxygen from the peroxides.

Let us, finally, introduce a few chemical equations, which may serve at least to illustrate the kind of chemical reactions that may be expected to occur [14]. The preparatory dark reaction is written down as a carboxylation reaction. The substance RH may, itself, be a carbohydrate if we accept the assumptions of Kamen and Ruben. Then there

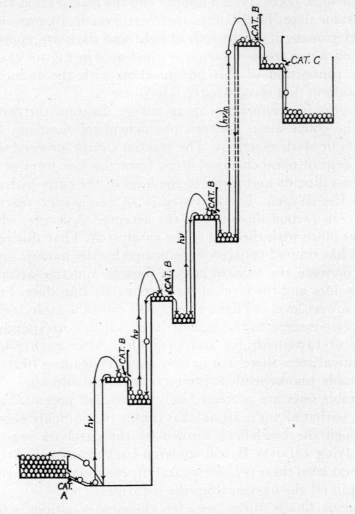

FIG. 92. Schematic representation of the course of the photochemical and catalytic reactions of photosynthesis.

follow eight photochemical steps. We assume here that they belong to two groups, one group in which, with the help of

$$RH \cdot CO_2 \xrightarrow{\text{Catalyst A}} RCOOH$$

1. RCOOH + H Chph* + hv $\xrightarrow{\text{Catalyst B}}$ Intermediate I + Chph
2. Intermediate I   "   "   "   "   II   "
3. Intermediate II   "   "   "   "   III   "
4. Intermediate III   "   "   " $(CH_2O)_6$ + Chph

5. Chph + ROH + hv $\xrightarrow{\text{Catalyst B}}$ H Chph + RO
6.   "   "   "   "   "   "
7.   "   "   "   "   "   "
8.   "   "   "   "   "   "

9. 2RO → ROOR

$$ROOR + H_2O \to + ROOH$$

$$2ROOH \xrightarrow{\text{Catalyst C}} ROH + O_2$$

* Symbol for nondehydrogenated chlorophyll.

the light energy absorbed by the chlorophyll, hydrogen atoms are transferred from the chlorophyll itself to the substance RCOOH, reducing it to a carbohydrate, while the four chlorophyll molecules are each deprived of one hydrogen atom. The mono-dehydro chlorophylls produced in this way must regain the hydrogen in order to be able to act again as hydrogen donors. It is assumed that this is done also with the help of a catalyst that takes away the hydrogen from an organic molecule ROH, transforming this substance into radicals which, by addition of water, form an organic peroxide. The peroxide may be attacked by catalyst C, which splits off oxygen and reproduces ROH.

It should be emphasized that this chemical picture serves only as an illustration. Future chemical experiments will certainly change the picture considerably, but one can hope that the main interaction between photochemical and catalytic reactions is correctly interpreted by the theory outlined above.

For References see p. 301.

THE STRUCTURE OF LIQUIDS

By JOHN G. KIRKWOOD

Cornell University

I

THE physical and chemical properties of liquids can be formally interpreted by means of thermodynamics and an empirical equation of state. From this point of view, it may be said that the liquid state has been adequately studied. Following the classic researches of van der Waals, many competent investigators have accumulated a large body of data on the equation of state of liquids and gases. However, the thermodynamic method fails to give insight into the structure of liquids on the molecular scale. It is our purpose to review certain recent experimental and theoretical investigations of the molecular structure of liquids and to discuss the information, as yet incomplete, which they provide.

On the experimental side, X-ray scattering has proved a most valuable tool for studying molecular distribution in liquids. The X-ray scattering technique has been used to great advantage in the study of molecular distribution in ordinary liquids, and also in glasses and other vitreous materials, which are to be regarded as undercooled liquids, thermodynamically metastable. On the theoretical side, the methods of statistical mechanics have been of value in clarifying the function of molecular structure and intermolecular forces in determining the statistical arrangement and distribution of molecules in liquids.

Fluidity and the inability to support shear stress are commonly regarded as the distinguishing characteristics of the liquid and gaseous states, as contrasted with solid state. Actually this is not a satisfactory criterion, for vitreous materials may possess rigidity, whereas crystalline solids may exhibit creep and plastic flow under shear at a measurable rate at elevated temperatures and high stress. Of more fundamental importance is the degree of order in the spatial arrangement and distribution of their component molecules, characteristic of the several states of aggregation. Liquids and gases are qualitatively similar in structure, and, in fact, the distinction between them vanishes entirely above the critical point. Their structures possess a certain degree of local order, the nature of which we shall presently discuss. Crystalline solids, on the other hand, possess a high degree of structural order extending over domains comprising many molecules.

In order to exhibit the points of similarity and difference in the structures of liquids and of crystalline solids, it is desirable to direct attention to crystal structure for the moment. By means of the techniques of X-ray crystallography, initiated by Von Laue and the Braggs, the structure of crystals has been exhaustively studied and is rather thoroughly understood. The structure of an ideal crystal at the absolute zero of temperature is characterized by a high degree of order and organization in the arrangement of its component atoms and molecules. This order is described by the theory of space lattices. There exists a fundamental unit of structure composed of a small number of atoms or molecules in a definite geometrical configuration. The crystal lattice is built up as a periodic reproduction of the fundamental unit in the three directions of space in a pattern resembling that of tiles in a floor.

As the temperature of a crystal is raised above absolute zero, various types of disorder may set in. The disorder may be macroscopic or microscopic in character. Mosaic structure and lattice dislocations are examples of macroscopic disorder extending over domains comprising many molecules. The simplest type of microscopic disorder produced by thermal motion is a displacement of the molecular centers from the equilibrium sites of the ideal lattice. When the amplitudes of the displacements are small, thermal disorder may be described by the theories of harmonic lattice vibrations due to Debye, Born, Karman, and Blackman, in which thermal motion is regarded as a superposition of elastic waves, qualitatively similar to ordinary sound waves, but of much higher frequency than sound waves excited by ordinary methods such as impact or piezo-electric oscillations. Lattice vibrational disorder ultimately disrupts the crystal lattice and leads to fusion.

The mechanism of the fusion process and the manner in which long-range crystalline order is destroyed have been clarified to some extent by recent theories of Lennard-Jones and Devonshire and of Kirkwood and Monroe. Long-range crystalline order is entirely absent in the liquid state resulting from fusion, and liquid structure cannot be referred to a space lattice. Nevertheless, a residue of local order, persisting as a memory of the highly organized crystalline structure, is maintained by each molecule in the distribution of neighbors in its immediate vicinity.

II

The local structural order characteristic of the liquid state may be described by means of the radial distribution function $g(R)$, defined as the ratio of the average local molecular density $\rho(R)$, at a distance R from an arbitrary molecule, to the bulk density ρ_0 of the liquid.

$$\rho(R) = \rho_0 \, g(R) \qquad (1)$$

A radial distribution function $g(R)$ equal to unity at all distances R corresponds to a completely random or disordered structure. Departures of $g(R)$ from the value unity measure the local order established by a molecule in the arrangement of its neighbors. For a typical liquid, $g(R)$ may be represented as a curve possessing a series of rapidly damped maxima and minima as shown in Figure 93. The positions of the maxima correspond roughly to the radii of the first several coördination shells in the crystalline state,

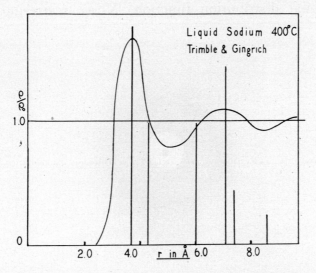

FIG. 93. Radial distribution function of liquid sodium. The vertical lines represent the relative densities of sodium atoms in the crystal lattice.

and the minima to intermediate distances between coördination shells. However, the residual order in the arrangement of the neighbors of a molecule in the liquid state lacks the sharpness of crystalline order and is appreciable only at distances of several molecular diameters. It is entirely insufficient to maintain long-range order characteristic of the crystal lattice. The resemblance of liquid structure to crystalline structure is, therefore, limited to a domain of molecular dimensions in the vicinity of any molecule.

The residual local order described by the radial distribution function can in no sense be regarded as static, but must be interpreted in a purely statistical sense. The neighbors of a specified molecule are being constantly interchanged with other molecules in the liquid, and large momentary fluctuations from the average density of neighbors $\rho(R)$ are to be expected.

The scattering of X rays by a liquid is directly related to the radial distribution function. X-ray scattering may,

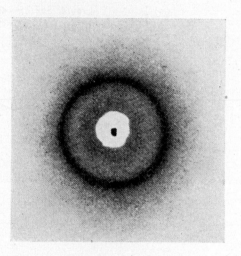

FIG. 94. X-ray scattering photograph of liquid rubidium.

therefore, be used as the basis for an experimental determination of the radial distribution function. The X-ray scattering technique for investigating liquid structure was developed by Zernicke and Prins and by Debye and Mencke. It has been used with great success by Warren and his coworkers as well as by many other investigators. The method may be briefly described in the following manner: A beam of monochromatic X rays is allowed to traverse a small sample of liquid in the form of a jet or confined in a glass capillary. The intensity of the scattered radiation is recorded as a function of scattering angle on a photographic plate, in an ionization chamber, or with the aid of a Geiger counter.

An X-ray scattering photograph of a liquid, as illustrated in Figure 94, resembles, to a certain extent, a Debye-Scherrer powder diagram of a crystalline solid. However, instead of the well-defined rings of maximum intensity of the powder diagram, a liquid gives only a few broad and diffuse rings of rapidly diminishing intensity. These similarities led Stewart to formulate his theory of cybotaxis, according to which a liquid is supposed to contain certain molecular groupings resembling minute crystallites. Stewart's point of view, if taken literally, is not entirely correct. However, there is no serious objection to the use of the term cybotaxis in referring to the residual local order statistically maintained by each molecule in its own environment.

From the intensity $I(\theta)$ of the X rays scattered by a liquid in a direction making an angle θ with the incident beam, the radial distribution function $g(R)$ may be computed in a very elegant manner with the use of the Fourier integral theorem. Using Warren's notation, we may express the relationship in the following manner:

$$g(R) - 1 = \frac{1}{2\pi^2 R} \int_{o}^{\infty} s\, i(s)\ \sin sR\, ds$$

$$(2)$$

$$i(s) = (I/Ie - Nf^2)/Nf^2; \quad s = \frac{4\pi}{\lambda} \sin \theta/2$$

where Ie is intensity of scattered radiation due to a single electron, λ the wave length of the X rays, and f the form factor of the atoms of which the liquid is composed. The Fourier integral of equation (2) is usually evaluated numerically or with the aid of an harmonic analyzer.

The radial distribution functions of many liquids and glasses have been determined by the X-ray scattering technique. We shall presently discuss the structural information provided by these studies. Although the Fourier inversion method for calculating the radial distribution function is strictly applicable only to a monatomic liquid, it can be employed in an approximate fashion to obtain worth-while qualitative information concerning the structure of poly-atomic liquids as well.

III

In the theoretical interpretation of the radial distribution function of a liquid, two methods have been employed. The first method is based upon the assumption that, although the long-range order of the lattice is absent in a liquid, the local arrangement of neighbors of each molecule can be regarded as a blurred reproduction of the first several coördination shells of neighbors of a single crystal lattice or of a superposition of several lattice types. The number of neighbors in each such blurred coördination shell is calculated as the integral of $4\pi R^2 \rho_0\, g(R)$ under the corresponding peak in the radial distribution function $g(R)$. This point of view has been developed extensively by Prins, Bernal, and more recently by Wall, Rushbrooke and Coulson, and Lennard-Jones and Corner. The second method is based on statistical mechanics. From statistical mechanical principles, an attempt is made to predict the form of the radial distribution function in a fluid composed of molecules interacting with known intermolecular forces. This method has been used by Mayer and by Kirkwood. Due to its complexity, it is difficult to apply except in the simplest cases. However, it provides a fundamental insight into the problem of liquid structure and clarifies the nature of phase transitions, as, for example, in the condensation of a gas and the fusion of a crystal.

Much valuable qualitative information can be obtained with the quasi-crystalline models of the local order in liquid structure. For example, the local molecular structure of liquid metals, such as mercury and sodium, corresponds to a close-packed arrangement of spheres. Bernal and Fowler have employed such a model with great success in interpreting the structure of liquid water. They assume tetrahedral coördination, each water molecule being linked to four neighbors by hydrogen bonds. By superposing coördination structures of the β-quartz, tridymite, and closed-packed type, they are able to construct a schematic radial distribution function which agrees substantially with the experimentally determined one. At low temperatures it appears that the β-quartz structure predominates. At high temperatures the proportion of the closed-packed contribution to the structure increases. Many of the anomalous properties of water, for example, the maximum density at $4°$ C., are accounted for by the Bernal-Fowler model. This model renders obsolete the earlier naïve theories of the structure of water based upon the idea of polymers such as dihydrol and trihydrol.

Warren has successfully interpreted the structure of the normal paraffin hydrocarbons in the liquid state. Their structure appears to be particularly simple, approximating the arrangement realized in the axial close-packing of slender rods. The X-ray scattering diagram of an aliphatic alcohol possesses an inner peak not observed for the corresponding hydrocarbons. This peak can be qualitatively interpreted if it is supposed that the alcohol molecules are linked in chains by hydrogen bonds between the hydroxyl groups, while the aliphatic radicals remain approximately close-packed as in the corresponding hydrocarbons. Similar qualitative interpretations of the structures of many organic liquids can be given.

When the problem of liquid structure is approached from the standpoint of statistical mechanics, it is found that the radial distribution function is only one of many molecular distribution functions that characterize the structure. However, the radial distribution function is of unique importance when the potential of intermolecular force can be regarded as a superposition of the interactions of molecular pairs. The general distribution function $\rho_n(R_1 \ldots R_n)$ specifies the probability that a set of n molecules will be found in a configuration $R_1 \ldots R_n$. In the general theory, the radial distribution function of a liquid is found to be identical with $\rho_2(R_1, R_2)$, the probability distribution function for molecular pairs.

Mayer's elegant statistical theory of the phenomenon of condensation is related to the general theory of distribution functions. This theory has clarified the mechanism of the phase transition between the vapor and liquid states, and has brought to light certain important facts concerning the critical point at which the distinction between gas and liquid vanishes. Recently Mayer and Montrol have discussed the definition and properties of the general molecular distribution function in a fluid system.

Using the general theory of distribution functions, Kirkwood and Monroe have recently developed a theory of the fusion of crystalline solids. A crystalline solid is characterized by a distribution function $\rho_1(R)$ which controls the long-range order of the crystal lattice. An integral equation has been formulated for the distribution function $\rho_1(R)$. At a constant value of the pressure, the equation is found at low temperature to have a periodic solution $\rho_1(R)$ with maxima at the lattice points of a crystal lattice. As the temperature increases the density maxima at the lattice points become progressively diffuse, due to thermal motion. Finally, above a certain temperature, which may be identified with the melting point, periodic solutions of the integral equation cease to exist, and long-range crystalline order in the molecular arrangement vanishes.

Although in the liquid long-range order does not exist, a

residual local order persists in the distribution function for molecular pairs, which, as we have pointed out, is identical with the radial distribution function. Again, using the general statistical mechanical theory of distribution functions, Kirkwood and Monroe have formulated and solved an in-

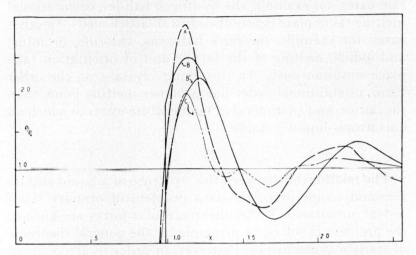

FIG. 95. Comparison of the theoretical and experimental radial distribution functions in liquid argon. Curve A, Miller and Lark-Horowitz. Curves B and B′, Theoretical, Kirkwood and Monroe. Curve C, Eisenstein and Gingrich.

tegral equation for the radial distribution function in a liquid composed of spherical molecules. Their theoretical distribution function for liquid argon has been compared with the experimental distribution functions of Lark-Horowitz and Miller and Eisenstein and Gingrich, and is found to agree with them to within the experimental error. The curves are shown in Figure 95.

Certain substances, for example, paraazoxyanisole, are capable of existence in a liquid crystalline state. A liquid crystalline phase possesses the fluidity of an ordinary liquid but is structurally anisotropic as is shown by its optical properties. The existence of liquid crystals can be under-

stood if the possibility of a long-range order in molecular
orientation is admitted. Long-range orientational order is
analogous to the long-range order in the arrangement of
molecular centers characteristic of a crystal lattice, and
may be expected to have a melting point of its own. In certain cases, for example, the hydrogen halides, orientational
melting takes place before the crystal lattice melts. In other
cases, for example, the pure halogens, chlorine, bromine,
and iodine, melting of the lattice and of orientation take
place simultaneously. In the liquid crystals, on the other
hand, orientational order has a higher melting point than
the lattice, and an interval of temperature exists in which an
anisotropic liquid is stable.

IV

The relationship between the structure of a liquid and its
thermodynamic properties is a problem of primary theoretical importance. If the intermolecular forces are known,
the problem is solved in principle by the general theorems
of statistical mechanics. However, in order to arrive at an
explicit solution, much complicated mathematical work is
necessary even when certain rather drastic approximations
are introduced.

Although, in principle, all of the general molecular distribution functions ρ_n are required for the specification of
the thermodynamic functions of a liquid, the equation of
state of a liquid composed of spherical molecules may be
expressed in terms of the radial distribution function alone,
when the total intermolecular force can be regarded as the
resultant of the superposition of forces between molecular
pairs. There is reason to believe that this is a good approximation for forces of the van der Waals type between chemically saturated molecules. The potential of intermolecular
force between a pair of molecules can, in principle, be calculated from a knowledge of their structure by means of

quantum mechanics. In practice it is frequently convenient to use an empirical expression of the type proposed by Lennard-Jones, for $V(R)$, the potential of intermolecular force between a pair of spherical molecules situated a distance R from each other,

$$V(R) = \frac{\lambda_1}{R^m} - \frac{\lambda_2}{R^6} \tag{3}$$

where λ_1 and λ_2 are constants, and m is an exponent in the neighborhood of 12. (See Fig. 96.) The second term, diminishing as the 6th power of the intermolecular distance, represents the van der Waals attraction between molecules, which is responsible for the general cohesive properties of matter. The first term represents a repulsive force, dominant at small intermolecular distances, which prevents molecules from interpenetrating to an appreciable extent and gives them an effective size.

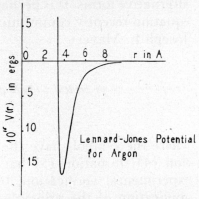

FIG. 96. The potential of intermolecular force for two argon atoms.

The latent heat of vaporization L of a liquid is related in a simple manner to the potential of intermolecular force $V(R)$ and the radial distribution function $g(R)$. The relationship is

$$L = RT - 2\pi N \rho_0 \int_0^\infty R^2 V(R) g(R) dR \tag{4}$$

where R is the gas constant, T the absolute temperature, N Avogadro's number, and ρ_0 the average molecular density. Equation 4, when applied to liquid argon at 90° K. with the Lennard-Jones potential and the experimental radial dis-

tribution function $g(R)$ determined from X-ray scattering
by Eisenstein and Gingrich, yields a value of the latent
heat of vaporization differing from the experimental value
only by .5 per cent.

The equation of state of a substance, or the relation between its pressure, p, volume v, and temperature T, together
with its specific heat suffices to determine its thermodynamic behavior. The relationship between the equation of
state of a liquid, the potential of intermolecular force, and
the radial distribution function can be expressed in several
alternative forms. It is perhaps most simply expressed by an
equation recently communicated to the writer by Professor
Joseph E. Mayer:

$$pv = RT - 2\pi N \rho_0 \int_0^\infty R^3 \frac{dV}{dR} g(R)dR \qquad (5)$$

where the symbols have the same significance as in equation (4). Equation (5) has not as yet been subjected to
experimental verification, but it is based upon an exact
application of the principles of statistical mechanics and
may be regarded as generally valid.

The statistical mechanical theory of liquid structure has
been approached from a somewhat different standpoint by
Eyring and Hirschfelder and Lennard-Jones and Devonshire. In these theories, explicit use is not made of the general theory of molecular distribution functions. Instead, a
compromise is made between the method of deduction from
the fundamental theorems of statistical mechanics and an
intuitive method based upon physical analogies. The theories of Eyring and of Lennard-Jones are designated as
the "free-volume" theories of the liquid state. The "free-
volume" theory is based upon the assumption that each
molecule in a liquid executes gaslike thermal motion in a

region of space called the free volume as illustrated in Figure 97. The free volume of a molecule is much smaller than the total volume of the liquid divided by the number of molecules, since each molecule is caged in by its neighbors.

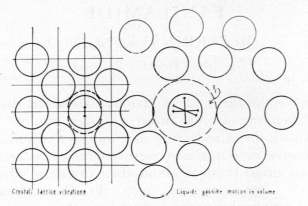

Crystal: lattice vibrations   Liquid: gas-like motion in volume

FIG. 97. Thermal motion according to the free-volume theories.

According to the "free-volume" theory, the equation of state of a liquid has the form,

$$p = RT \frac{d \log v_t}{dv} - \frac{dE}{dv} \qquad (6)$$

where v_f is the free volume per molecule, v the total volume, and E is the internal energy of the liquid. The different free-volume theories prescribe different models upon which to base the calculation of v_f. These theories have been very successful in reproducing the empirical equations of state of many liquids.

From the brief survey attempted in this chapter, we hope that the reader may have gained certain information of general interest concerning the methods and results of modern investigations of the structure of liquids on the molecular scale.

For References see p. 302.

IX

THE MODE OF ACTION OF SUL-
FANILAMIDE

By PERRIN H. LONG, M.D.

The Johns Hopkins University

THE problem of the mode of action of antiseptic drugs has always been one of great interest, and it was only natural that with the introduction of prontosil and sulfanilamide intensive investigations were instituted to determine how these drugs brought about their dramatic effects. In Domagk's original report upon the chemotherapeutic effects of prontosil in experimental hemolytic streptococcal infections in mice, the fact that the drug was effective only in living organisms was stressed, as was also its lack of effect on bacteria in cultures outside the body. This observation has been repeatedly confirmed in respect to both prontosil and its companion azodye, neoprontosil.

This divergence between the in vitro and in vivo activity of prontosil puzzled the earlier observers and led to the formation of certain hypotheses regarding the action of the drug. Levaditi and Vaisman first considered the possibility that the drug activated host defense mechanisms; next that it prevented the formation of capsules, thus rendering the virulent streptococci susceptible to phagocytosis; and finally, late in 1935, that the drug probably acted upon susceptible microörganisms in a way that lessened their defenses against those of the host. Domagk, on the contrary, held that prontosil per se or a conversion product of this drug acted directly upon susceptible bacteria in vivo. In his latest report this observer stated that "the first phase of action consisted always of an attack directly upon the germs, but the microbes were rarely completely destroyed, being more often sufficiently modified to be destroyed by means of the defense mechanism of the host." Thus, according to Domagk, the streptococci in prontosil-treated animals behaved like avirulent streptococci.

Little progress in this problem was made until late in 1935, when the Trefouels, Nitti, and Bovet announced that it was their belief that prontosil broke down in the animal body to triaminobenzene and para-aminobenzene sulfonamide (sulfanilamide), and that they had found the latter compound to be an active chemotherapeutic agent in the control of experimental streptococcal infections in mice. This obviously was an observation second in importance only to that of Domagk, because it showed that the azo linkage was unnecessary for therapeutic activity and provided the needed steppingstone for further investigations of the mode of action of these compounds.

However, as has been pointed out, "to show that sulfanilamide is an effective chemotherapeutic agent is a far call from proving that it is the active component of prontosil." Nevertheless, evidence was soon produced that this might be the case when Fourneau, the Trefouels, Nitti, and Bovet reported that the addition of sulfanilamide to cultures of *Aspergillus niger* delayed the growth of these organisms in Raulin's medium, thus demonstrating for the first time the in vitro bacteriostatic activity of sulfanilamide. This observation is the keystone upon which rests the major structure of subsequent work dealing with the mode of action of sulfanilamide and its derivatives. It has been confirmed by numerous observers working with a wide variety of microörganisms.

Another link in the chain of evidence that sulfanilamide was the active molecule in prontosil was the demonstration by Colebrook and his associates and by ourselves that the reduction of neoprontosil in vivo or in vitro results in the production of a bacteriostatic substance and, as was shown by Fuller, that the effective material liberated both in vitro and in vivo from the neoprontosil molecule in the course of reduction is sulfanilamide.

It is important to point out here that there have been numerous objectors to the theory that prontosil and neo-prontosil are active only by virtue of their reduction to sulf-anilamide. Domagk opposed this belief, first, because he was unable to find any great difference in the in vitro bac-teriostatic activity of prontosil and sulfanilamide (an obser-vation at variance with the experience of practically all other observers and due to marked technical differences in the conduct of his experiments) ; second, because he consid-ered that the presence of sulfanilamide in the urine of patients receiving prontosil was no indication that it was the active fraction of the dye compound; and finally, be-cause the liberation of sulfanilamide during the course of prontosil therapy was not proof that it was the active frac-tion, inasmuch as there were a number of therapeutically active compounds which could not possibly liberate sulfan-ilamide. This last argument is extremely weak, since no one has claimed that sulfanilamide is the only conceivable active compound.

Although we do not intend to dwell at length upon the relation of chemical structure to therapeutic activity, a few observations are worth mentioning for the light they throw on this subject.

It seems quite likely, as just indicated, that the activity of the azo compounds is dependent upon the destruction of the $N=N$ linkage in the body and the subsequent forma-tion of sulfanilamide. The amino group in benzene sulfon-amide compounds must be para to the sulfonamide group. Meta- and ortho-amino compounds are inactive. Substitu-tions in the amino group of sulfanilamide generally lower the effectiveness of the compound; and, as far as our observations go, the activity of any sulfanilamide derivative containing the NH-R group is dependent upon the splitting-off of the R radical, and the subsequent reversion of the compound to sulfanilamide. (The possible exception to the rule would be the hydroxylamine derivative.) It has also been demonstrated that the para amino group is not necessary for activity, as paranitrobenzene sulfonamide is an effective compound. (The stability of this derivative in vivo is still a matter of discussion.)

Substitutions in the sulfonamide group (SO_2NH-R) may or may not result in a compound showing a lowered degree of activity. For example, sulfapyridine is a highly effective compound, whereas N(p-aminobenzene sulfonyl)-1, 4-oxazine is practically without activity. As far as is known, most of the compounds resulting from substitutions made in the sulfonamide group are stable and, if active, derive their effect from the whole molecule. In other words, the SO_2NH-R linkage is firm. It has also been demonstrated that the SO_2NH_2 group is not the only active radical and that the S, SO, and SO_2 groups possess varying degrees of activity, provided they are placed para to the amino group. Mayer and Oechslin have shown that sulfur-containing radicals are unnecessary for activity, by demonstrating the chemotherapeutic effectiveness of paranitrobenzoic acid in the treatment of experimental streptococcal infections.

Therefore it can be assumed from what is known that the molecules of sulfanilamide and sulfapyridine, while possibly undergoing oxidative changes in the body (at least according to certain theories regarding their mode of action), do not suffer radical alterations in their chemical structure during their period of activity in the body of the infected host. Hence it is highly likely that the way in which sulfanilamide acts upon susceptible microörganisms is similar to the action of sulfapyridine, the variations being only in the intensity of action.

In discussing the mode of action of sulfanilamide and sulfapyridine, it should be borne in mind that, although their activity appears to be directed solely against the invading microörganism, the recovery of the infected subject seems to entail two factors: the drug factor and the host factor. That is to say, while the drug can bring the infection under control, it requires the coöperation of the host's defense mechanism to dispose of the infectious agent. This statement is in agreement with the conception of those investigators who have attacked the problem by studying the in vitro and in vivo effects of these drugs.

Under the heading of the drug factor comes the activity of these compounds in inhibiting the growth of, or possibly actually killing, susceptible bacteria, and their ability to neutralize the harmful effects of the toxic products of certain microörganisms. The host factor represents the response of the body's defense mechanisms, such as antibody production and mobilization of phagocytic cells, to the infection produced by microörganisms that have been altered as a direct result of the drug factor.

At the present time it is possible to select from the welter of conflicting opinions three main hypotheses concerning the manner in which sulfanilamide and sulfapyridine exert their bacteriostatic effect upon susceptible bacteria. The first of these is based upon data which are believed to indicate that oxidative changes, in which molecular oxygen plays a role, are responsible for the conversion of sulfanilamide or sulfapyridine into "truly" active compounds.

Early in 1937 Mayer concluded that as sulfanilamide appeared to be less active in vitro than in vivo, one must postulate the formation of a more active compound in the body. This he claimed must be an oxidation product (the process being brought about by an oxidant in the body). In support of his hypothesis, Mayer cited the frequent appearance of methemoglobinemia in patients receiving sulfanilamide, an occurrence which, according to him, implied the presence of an agent capable of oxidizing hemoglobin. Sulfanilamide would be unable to do this, but its first oxidation product, para-hydroxylaminobenzene sulfonamide, could bring about this change. He next synthesized para-hydroxylaminobenzene sulfonamide and reported that its bacteriostatic activity was about one hundred times that of sulfanilamide in vitro. In addition, Mayer stated that other oxidation products of sulfanilamide, such as azoxy, nitro, and nitroso derivatives, were also highly active compounds. Little, however, was done immediately to prove or disprove Mayer's hypothesis because of the difficulties surrounding the preparation of the hydroxyl derivative of sulfanilamide.

About a year after Mayer's report was published, Ottenberg and Fox noted that irradiated dilute solutions of sulfanilamide turned blue. Later they reported that this phenomenon did not occur in the absence of oxygen and that the blue substance could be reduced to a colorless product, thus indicating that the existence of an oxidation-reduction system. However, they were unable to demonstrate that the blue substance possessed bacteriostatic activity or that the reduction product was sulfanilamide.

Fox, German, and Janeway studied the effects of the addition of sulfanilamide upon electrode potentials in sterile broth (which were unaffected) and in cultures of hemolytic streptococci. They found that, whereas the electrode potential in such cultures fell rapidly during normal growth, it remained elevated during the time that sulfanilamide was exerting its bacteriostatic effect. In the presence of cysteine, or when air was excluded by sealing the cultures with vaseline, the potential was lowered despite the addition of sulfanilamide, and the bacteriostatic activity of the drug was definitely decreased.

Warren, Street, and Stokinger, unlike Fox and his associates, did observe an elevation of the potential of sterile broth to which sulfanilamide had been added, but they doubted that the drug poised the system at a "critical" E_h. They too found that the electrode potentials of cultures of streptococci fell less rapidly in the presence of sulfanilamide. They noted that when the drug was added to 21-hour-old cultures, a rapid rise in potential occurred, and that under anaerobic conditions there was no difference between the potentials of the control and sulfanilamide cultures. The same was true in the presence of cysteine, and in such cultures the bacteriostatic activity of sulfanilamide was reduced to a minimum. These investigators did not reach any definite conclusions as a result of their observations, but suggested that it was possible that sulfanilamide inactivated enzyme systems by attacking sulfhydryl or similar groups which are "normally responsible for the attainment of highly negative potentials."

Two years ago Shaffer advanced the hypothesis that sulfanilamide is oxidized in the presence of hydrogen peroxide, plus essential catalysts, to an active compound. This product is so strong an oxidant that it destroys catalase, thereby permitting more hydrogen peroxide to accumulate. As a result more and more of the oxidation product of sulfanilamide is formed, until eventually a concentration is reached sufficient to attack all reactive reducing systems of the cell, and bacteriostasis of actual killing of the microörganisms ensues.

The second hypothesis dealing with the mode of action of sulfanilamide was advanced by Locke, Main, Mellon, and Shinn. These observers noted that dilute solutions of sulfanilamide, which had been irradiated with ultraviolet light, possessed the property of inactivating catalase. It has been long known that if catalase is inactivated in aerobic cultures of pneumococci, peroxide accumulates rapidly and

may reach a concentration that is bactericidal for the pneumococcal cells. Hence, they reasoned that if sulfanilamide
was able to inactivate catalase, peroxide would accumulate,
and this factor might account for the bacteriostatic or bactericidal action of sulfanilamide.

They described the mechanism as follows:

The growing bacterial cell has the power to convert sulfanilamide,
presumably through mild oxidation, into a derivative which is a highly
active anticatalase. This reaction produces an accumulation of anticatalase in the immediate vicinity of the cell. The streptococcus and
pneumocooccus, being active producers of hydrogen peroxide, are able
to grow only so long as the peroxide concentration can be kept below
a critical level by outward diffusion, or destruction . . . in the presence
of anticatalase, inactivation of catalase takes place in the zone immediately adjacent to the cell with resultant accumulation of hydrogen
peroxide to toxic levels.

In support of this view they brought forth evidence to
show that peroxide accumulated to higher concentrations
in pneumococcal cultures containing sulfanilamide than in
cultures without sulfanilamide, and that if there was a "reduction of the percentage of oxygen in the superambient
air of broth cultures of the Type I pneumococcus," the bacteriostatic effects of sulfanilamide were either greatly reduced or altogether prevented. However, they also found
that when the oxygen concentration was reduced to below
0.04 per cent (not even approaching anaerobiosis!) sulfanilamide was again a strongly bacteriostatic agent in cultures of pneumococci. They further reported that they had
observed chain formation in sulfanilamide-containing cultures of pneumococci and suggested that "the nature of this
change is reminiscent of the morphology assumed by the
avirulent R. culture phase of the pneumococcus."

Before discussing the third explanation offered for the
mode of action of sulfanilamide, we should like to point out
that the two hypotheses just discussed are based upon a sup-

posed oxidation of sulfanilamide to an active derivative and that an important point in support of this belief is the claim that sulfanilamide and sulfapyridine are inactive under anaerobic conditions. Hence, if it could be shown that sulfanilamide and sulfapyridine are effective bacteriostatic agents under conditions of strict anaerobiosis, this would constitute a definite objection to both the oxidation and anticatalase theories, since both are based upon the assumption that molecular oxygen is necessary for the reaction.

Early in 1937 we demonstrated that the reduction of neoprontosil could be brought about by the addition of an excess of cysteine hydrochloride and that the resulting sulfanilamide was bacteriostatic against the C203 strain of hemolytic streptococci even though marked reducing conditions prevailed in the medium. Later in the same year we described the bacteriostatic effects of sulfanilamide in anaerobic cultures of *Cl. welchii*. This latter observation has been confirmed by Sadusk and Manahan.

Recently we have studied the bacteriostatic effects of sulfanilamide and sulfapyridine upon hemolytic streptococci and pneumococci under various conditions of anaerobiosis. These tests were conducted with rigid precautions to secure anaerobiosis and in each instance the reduction of methylene blue was used as an indication that an aerobiosis had been obtained. It is evident from the data obtained that the bacteriostatic effects of sulfanilamide upon a strain of Type I pneumococcus and upon the C203 strain of Group A hemolytic streptococci were quite good under anaerobic conditions. When sulfapyridine was used as the bacteriostatic agent there was no difference between the effects noted under aerobic and anaerobic conditions in the pneumococcal cultures (in the majority of tests sulfapyridine sterilized the cultures irrespective of their oxygen content) and there was only a slight difference when the streptococcus was the test organism.

Regardless of the reason for the disagreement between our results and those of other workers who have studied the effect of anaerobiosis upon the bacteriostatic action of sulfanilamide, the fact that we obtained definite bacteriostasis with sulfanilamide and actual killing with sulfapyridine in the absence of air tends to discredit the concept that these drugs are activated by molecular oxygen. Obviously, if anaerobic conditions prevail, hydrogen peroxide cannot be formed from bacteria, as has been postulated. As a matter of record, our experience is in complete harmony with that of Shinn, Main, and Mellon who found that at concentrations of less than 0.04 per cent of oxygen, sulfanilamide exerted a bacteriostatic effect in cultures of pneumococci.

Another observation that throws light upon the importance of peroxide in the mechanism of action of sulfanilamide was made by Fuller and Maxted, who noted that Type III, Group A hemolytic streptococci as a class fail to produce hydrogen peroxide. It just happens that the strains "Richards" and C203 are Type III hemolytic streptococci and have been shown by Fuller and Maxted and ourselves not to produce detectable amounts of peroxide in cultures. Nevertheless, both of these strains have been demonstrated to be very sensitive to the bacteriostatic activity of sulfanilamide. As Fuller and Maxted have stated, these observations constitute "an apparently insuperable objection" to the hypothesis of Locke and his associates.

A third theory dealing with the mode of action of sulfanilamide is based upon the idea that the drug acts on bacteria to prevent them from utilizing the substrate or upon the substrate to prevent it from being utilized by the bacteria. In 1937 we suggested that sulfanilamide brought about changes in the metabolism of the streptococcus and stated that it was our belief that the drug acted directly upon this microörganism. Later in the same year Levaditi advanced the hypothesis that sulfanilamide combined with the body proteins of the host to form a drug-protein complex which was unassimilable by bacteria. Although Mellon and Bambas stated that the drug had no effect upon the hydrogenase of the pneumococcus for glucose, Barron and Jacobs observed that 0.2 per cent sulfanilamide inhibited to a small degree the oxidation of glucose by hemolytic streptococci and of glucose and lactate by Friedlander's bacilli, and Chu and Hastings reported that 0.66 grams of sulfanilamide "invariably reduced the oxygen up-take" of tissues (rat diaphragm and liver and human blood) as well as of beta hemolytic streptococci, gonococci, pneumococci Types I and II, and meningococci. A concentration of 0.0132 grams per cent was effective only in the case of the meningococcus. These observations pointed to the fact that the drug acted directly upon certain of the metabolic processes of microörganisms.

At about this time Lockwood made an important observation in respect to the mode of action of sulfanilamide. He observed that the addition of small amounts of peptone to human serum cultures of beta hemolytic streptococci definitely decreased the bactericidal and, in some instances, the bacteriostatic effects of the drug upon virulent hemolytic streptococci. This observation led him to suggest "that sulfanilamide prevents the specialized metabolic activity required of invasive organisms" and "that this effect may be achieved through prevention of the utilization of the protein substrate of the organisms." He further showed that peptone had a similar protective effect against the action of sulfanilamide and sulfapyridine upon the pneumococcus in human serum and upon *E. coli* in urine cultures. These observations opened new possibilities for the exploration of the field of the mode of action of sulfanilamide, and pointed the way toward two possibilities: first, that peptone produced the antisulfanilamide effect by acting simply as a growth stimulant; and second, that peptone actually contained or was the precursor of a substance which would inactivate the bacteriostatic effect of sulfanilamide.

Dr. Eleanor Bliss and I were very much interested in Lockwood's observations and soon we were able to confirm them. Our next step was to make a systematic study of the factors involved in the so-called antisulfanilamide effect of peptone. In order to do this, we selected *E. coli* as the test organism and used a purely synthetic medium throughout the experiments. We first tested numerous brands of peptones and found that in varying degree all possessed the power of altering the bacteriostatic effects of sulfanilamide upon *E. coli* in the synthetic medium. We then tested the effect of further split products of protein such as proteoses, "Aminoids," etc. All of these substances showed a considerable ability to neutralize the effect of sulfanilamide on the test organism in the synthetic medium. The possibility was next explored that either a single amino acid or combinations of amino acids might exert a similar effect to that noted for the split products of protein. More than a year ago we reported that an amino acid (methionine) inhibited the bacteriostatic effects of sulfanilamide upon *E. coli* in a simple synthetic medium. During the past year we have carefully restudied this whole problem from the point of view of whether or not the antisulfanilamide effect of methionine could be attributed directly to growth stimulation or whether it represented a true antisulfanilamide effect. After numerous experiments which will be reported in detail shortly, we have come to the conclusion that methionine, while showing slight growth-stimulating effects in certain concentrations, also acts as a true inhibitor of the bacteriostatic effects of sulfanilamide upon *E. coli*.

While this work was in progress, other observations were reported that tended to show that sulfanilamide exerted its effect by interfering with the metabolism of susceptible bacteria. MacLeod noted that, while sulfapyridine did not interfere with the dehydrogenase of the pneumococcus for glucose, it did inhibit the dehydrogenases for glycerol, lactate, and peruvate. In 1939 Stamp made a most interesting observation when he reported that an alkaline extract of a normally sulfanilamide-susceptible strain of hemolytic streptococcus had the property of inhibiting the action of sulfanilamide on the homologous and other strains of hemolytic streptococci when they were grown in Hartley broth. This extract stimulated the growth of streptococci in broth in the absence of sulfanilamide. Because of the presence of numerous protein degradation products in the medium, he did not consider that the antisulfanilamide factor was an amino acid (unless it was one of the rare amino acids which the organisms ordinarily have to synthesize). Therefore, he concluded that this extract might contain a substance which was an essential part of an enzyme system and suggested that it might be a coenzyme.

Shortly after Stamp's work was reported, Green observed that extracts of *Brucella abortus* yielded a potent growth-promoting factor which possessed a marked ability to eliminate the bacteriostatic effects of sulfanilamide. He also noted that a similar fraction which antagonized the bacteriostatic action of sulfanilamide could be extracted from many other bacteria. Interestingly enough, he did not observe a similar effect from yeast extract, meat extract, casein digest, or in five brands of peptone. Thiamin, nicotinic acid, beta alanine, beta indoleacetic acid, pimelic acid, glutamin, uracil, cysteine, inositol, and biotin were found by Green to be negative for the antisulfanilamide factor. Two out of four samples of concentrated liver extract showed a slight antisulfanilamide activity. A review of his experiments led Green to interpret his findings as follows: "The conclusion seems warranted that the "P" (for pullulating)-factor catalyzes and sulfanilamide inhibits some fundamental chemical reaction which is intimately concerned with bacterial reproduction." He considered that the reaction might well be enzymic in nature and that the P-factor might play the part of a coenzyme as had been previously suggested by Stamp. Shortly after Green's paper appeared, Fleming stated that he too had found that extracts from a number of different bacteria had an anti-sulfanilamide effect and that he believed this phenomenon was possibly related to Lockwood's observations concerning the effect of peptone.

In April, 1940, D. D. Woods reported some extremely interesting observations to the effect that para amino benzoic acid inactivated the bacteriostatic effect of sulfanilamide. In Wood's opinion sulfanilamide produced its effect by interfering with some substance essential for the metabolism of the bacterial cell, and he suggested that para amino benzoic acid was such a substance. He inferred that under ordinary conditions the required para amino benzoic acid is synthesized by bacteria growing in an adequate medium. Hence, in completely adequate media, sulfanilamide in ordinary concentrations is at best only bacteriostatic and insofar as certain organisms are concerned is practically ineffective in inhibiting their multiplication. However, in poor media in whch the synthesis of this compound is difficult for the microörganisms, sulfanilamide is highly effective as a bacteriostatic agent and may be even bactericidal. Woods suggested that the enzyme reaction involved in the utilization of para amino benzoic acid by the organisms is subject to competitive inhibition by sulfanilamide and that this inhibition is due to a structural relationship between sulfanilamide and para amino benzoic acid. Woods considered that the "Stamp factor" contained para amino benzoic acid, and he himself demonstrated that yeast extracts contained a substance which reversed the inhibitory action of sulfanilamide upon hemolytic streptococci. In a subsequent report, Selbie showed that para amino benzoic acid antagonized the curative effects of sulfanilamide in experimental streptococcal infections in mice, thus revealing that the drug was an effective antisulfanilamide agent not only in vitro but also in vivo. These observations of Woods and Selbie have been widely confirmed.

Shortly after the appearance of Woods's paper, West and Coburn reported that sulfapyridine modified the normal metabolism of staphylococci and came to the conclusion that under the conditions of their experiments sulfapyridine and nicotinic acid competed for the same position in the co-enzyme molecule, so that in the presence of sulfapyridine the organism was unable to form a coenzyme, and the activity of certain dehydrogenases was inhibited. If a co-enzyme was supplied (in the form of highly purified yeast coenzyme), the normal metabolism of the staphylococcus was not modified by sulfapyridine, and growth curves appeared to follow the customary pattern. Dorfman, *et al.*, noted a similar effect from sulfapyridine in respect to its action on the dysentery bacillus.

These concepts of the action of sulfapyridine were in harmony with that of Fildes who stated that according to his theory an antibacterial agent should be capable of either combining with an essential metabolite, thus forming a product devoid of the essential metabolite function, or of blocking an enzyme specifically associated with the metabolite. In the latter instance one would expect the antibacterial substance to have a chemical similarity to its competitor in the enzyme system. The findings of Woods, West, and Coburn and of Dorfman and his associates were in line with Fildes's theories because of the chemical similarity of para amino benzoic acid to sulfanilamide and of nicotinic acid to sulfapyridine.

MacLeod has recently studied various sources of inhibitor substances for sulfapyridine. He has shown that such substances can be demonstrated in extracts of fresh normal muscle, pancreas, and spleen of certain animals, and that after the autolysis of such tissues the amount of inhibitor substance is greatly increased. Active inhibitor was not present in fresh liver from beef, rabbit, or guinea pig, but was demonstrable in autolysates of such tissues. Normal human urine contained little or no active inhibitor, but upon acid hydrolysis considerable amounts of inhibitor were demonstrated. Inhibitor substances were noted uniformly in pus, but none were found in blood serum. According to MacLeod's findings, in certain species of microörganisms the inhibitor was found in the cells only, whereas in others the inhibitors were present in the culture supernatant, and the cells themselves were quite free.

It is obvious from the observations just recorded that the inhibitor substance first noted by Lockwood and subsequently by Stamp, Green, Woods, *et al.*, is quite widespread in nature and that in its biological reactions in respect to sulfanilamide it closely resembles para amino benzoic acid. However, this latter chemical was not demonstrated in nature until Rubbo and Gillespie reported upon the extraction of para amino benzoic acid in a pure form from Brewer's yeast. It is to be remembered that Woods assumed this compound must be a growth factor for various bacteria. Rubbo and Gillespie next showed that para amino benzoic acid was a definite growth factor for *Clostridium acetobutylicum* when the organism was grown in a synthetic medium. This observation brought about the reinforcement that was lacking for the acceptance of the views of Woods and Fildes because it definitely proved that para amino benzoic acid was a growth factor for microörganisms. An interesting corollary observation has recently been made by Ansbacher who reported that a certain type of gray hair produced on the bellies of mice as a result of a deficient diet could be prevented by the addition of para amino benzoic acid to the diet, thus showing that this compound has properties which permit it to be considered a vitamin.

Another problem connected with the mode of action of sulfanilamide and its derivatives concerns the effect of these compounds upon the soluble toxins and the toxic products of various bacteria. Bosse was probably the first to report that the presence of prontosil decreased the hemolysin production of streptococci. This was confirmed by Levaditi and Vaisman, who in addition concluded that prontosil and neoprontosil prevented the in vitro action of streptococcal leucocidin.

However, other observers have failed to demonstrate a neutralizing effect by sulfanilamide or neoprontosil upon the soluble "toxins" of the streptococcus in vitro. Thus, while this phase of the question is subject to dispute, there can be little doubt that the findings of King and his associates—which demonstrated that in a 1:1,000 concentration neoprontosil, though not bacteriostatic, did cause a lowering of the hemolytic index of streptococci grown in rabbit plasma—rabbit red-cell clots—are of great interest, especially so since sulfanilamide did not produce this effect.

In 1937 Levaditi and Vaisman reported that the endotoxins of the gonococcus, meningococcus, and *B. aertrycke* could be neutralized in vivo by sulfanilamide and certain of its derivatives. Staphylococcal toxin was, on the other hand, unaffected by these drugs. These observations have been confirmed and extended by Carpenter and his associates, who have shown that not only is gonococcal toxin neutralized both in vitro and in vivo by sulfanilamide, but so are the toxins of *Staphylococcus aureus, Cl. welchii,* and *Cl. tetani.* They have also demonstrated that the administration of neoprontosil by the *oral* route (but not when injected parenterally) protected the majority of mice against lethal doses of the toxins of the gonococcus, the hemolytic streptococcus, *Staphylococcus aureus, Cl. welchii,* and *Cl.*

botulinus. During the past three years we have attempted at various times to repeat the observations of Carpenter and his associates. So far we have been unsuccessful in confirming the observations of those workers who believe that the sulfonamide group of drugs is capable of neutralizing certain bacterial toxins and endotoxins both in vitro and in vivo.

In discussing the host factor it must at once be pointed out that there is no experimental evidence that sulfanilamide or its derivatives *stimulate* the activity of the reticulo-endothelial system. The activity of the phagocytes or antibodies is generally a secondary (although in some instances a very important) effect of sulfanilamide therapy.

Domagk remarked upon the essentially normal appearance of the leucocytes in peritoneal exudates from mice which had been infected with streptococci and treated with prontosil. However, it was Levaditi who first pointed out that the phagocytosis of streptococci might play an important part in the recovery of mice infected with these organisms and treated with prontosil. This observation has subsequently been confirmed by almost all those who have studied the effects of sulfanilamide therapy upon the cellular response in animals infected with virulent Group A hemolytic streptococci.

During the past three years we have been very much interested in trying to determine what happens to the infecting microörganisms in animals that have been treated with sulfanilamide and its derivatives. Early in our studies we noted that if the streptococcal peritonitis, which can be produced by the intraperitoneal injection of 1,000 M.L.D. of strain C203, was permitted to develop to a stage in which from 1 to 5 coccal units could be seen in an oil-immersion field of the stained peritoneal exudate, and then treatment with sulfanilamide was started, two phenomena were observed. The first was that within 2 to 4 hours the multiplication of the cocci in the peritoneal exudates of the treated animals was definitely retarded; in other words, the drug's bacteriostatic effect became apparent. Secondly, with bacteriostasis, an increase in phagocytosis over that already existing was noted. If treatment was continued, the number of extracellular cocci steadily decreased as phagocytosis increased, until a point was reached when the exudate was free from visible streptococci. In contradistinction to the observation that, although phagocytosis might be quite brisk in the untreated mice, the ingested cocci multiplied within the cells and frequently destroyed them, was the finding that in the treated mice the streptococci did not multiply within the cells and were soon digested by the phagocytes.

The chain of events just described is that noted in mice which received a relatively small inoculum of hemolytic streptococci and in which the infection was allowed to progress naturally for a period of 6 to 8 hours before treatment was started. If, instead of this, the mice are treated on the day before and again 1 hour before being infected, and the infecting dose is large (about 5 million organisms), although a moderate degree of bacteriostasis and some phagocytosis may be noted in smears from the peritoneal exudate, the streptococci multiply rapidly and the mice succumb in from 12 to 16 hours.

However, if the streptococci have been grown for two or three generations in 20 mg. per cent sulfanilamide or sulfapyridine blood broth before being injected into the pretreated and subsequently treated mice, bacteriostasis and phagocytosis of the cocci begin almost at once, and within a few hours the peritoneal exudate is clear of streptococci. In untreated control animals the "pretreated" streptococci quickly regain their natural characteristics and the animals succumb within 10 to 24 hours. This experiment, when taken in conjunction with the previous series, shows that the prior injection of sulfanilamide or sulfa-pyridine into mice does not activate the drug, and that pre-treatment of the streptococci with the drug makes them immediately susceptible to the effects of the drug when they are injected into mice which have been treated.

If the mouse is deprived of its polymorphonuclear leuco-cytes, as can be done by the administration of benzene, ade-quate therapy with sulfanilamide is unavailing; the strep-tococci multiply slowly and the mouse dies in from 3 to 4 days. This indicates that bacteriostasis alone is insufficient and that the presence of the leucocytes is necessary if the infection is to be brought under control.

It might be asked: Do not other host factors, such as the development of antibodies, come into play in the recovery of these mice? As far as anyone has been able to show, they do not. Mice which have recovered from a hemolytic strepto-coccal infection as a result of sulfanilamide therapy are as susceptible to reinfection with the homologous organism as are normal mice. Hence it seems that in mice the bac-teriostatic activity of the drug, coupled with the resulting phagocytosis, is the essential factor in recovery from Group A hemolytic streptococcal infection. In human beings this factor is certainly of great importance, but inasmuch as studies of the immune responses of patients ill with hemo-lytic streptococcal infections and treated with sulfanilamide have not been reported, we cannot say with certainty that it represents the whole host factor.

A second type of host response is noted in mice infected with virulent pneumococci. We have previously shown that both sulfanilamide and 4:4' diamino diphenyl sulfone exerted a bacteriostatic effect upon the growth of pneumo-cocci in the peritoneal cavities of mice, and that despite this bacteriostasis little phagocytosis was noted. The pneumo-cocci multiplied at a definitely slower rate in the treated animals than in the controls, but all the mice eventually died. It was also shown that the lack of phagocytosis was not the result of damage to the phagocytic cells, for when conditions were made favorable by injecting type-specific antipneumococcal serum, a wave of phagocytosis was noted.

Buttle had found that mice which survived after being infected with fairly large numbers of pneumococci and treated with the benzylidene derivative of diamino diphenyl sulfone were immune to subsequent infection with the homologous type of pneumococcus. Whitby confirmed this observation (as we have also) when sulfapyridine was used in the treatment of experimental pneumococcal infections in mice.

It therefore seemed from these observations that the mechanism of recovery, through the agency of drug therapy, differed in experimental pneumococcal and streptococcal infections in mice. A series of experiments designed to furnish evidence upon this question shows that if mice are pretreated with sulfapyridine and then infected with a highly virulent (but sulfapyridine-susceptible) strain of Type I pneumococci, a definite multiplication of the cocci occurs for the first 4 to 6 hours. Then (provided the treatments are kept up) a change takes place and, with but a minor degree of phagocytosis, the number of cocci rapidly decreases until practically none can be found in the peritoneal exudate at the end of 48 hours. What happens to the pneumococci during this period of decrease is unknown. They may be killed by the drug, but there is no evidence for this assumption. All that can be stated with certainty is that they are not engulfed by the phagocytes. We do know, however, that if treatment is discontinued too soon, the infection will recur promptly and the mice will die, although the peritoneal exudate is free of cocci. Hence it is necessary to continue treatment for about 5 days if permanent survivals are desired.

If, as with the streptococci, the pneumococci are grown

for one or two generations in blood broth containing 20 mg. per cent of sulfapyridine and are then injected into mice which have been pretreated and are treated with sulfa-pyridine, bacteriostasis begins almost immediately and the cocci slowly disappear from the exudate. Here again the phagocytes do not appear to have a prominent function in the removal of the pneumococci. Also, as in the previous experiment, if treatment is stopped when the exudate is just clear of pneumococci, a recurrence of the infection will almost invariably follow.

It seems quite clear in experimental pneumococcal infec-tions that while the drug is holding the infecting organisms in check, the latter must be acting antigenically to bring about the type-specific immunization of the animal. Hence, if treatment is continued until the animal is well immun-ized, recovery from the infection is permanent. That this is probably true in human beings also is evident from the observations of Wood and Long, who noted in patients ill with pneumococcal lobar pneumonia and treated with sulfapyridine that, although the therapy might bring about a rapid apparent recovery, recurrences of the infection were to be expected if sulfapyridine was discontinued before a type-specific antipneumococcal antibody appeared in their sera.

It may therefore be stated that the host response to chemotherapy in pneumococcal infections differs in both the experimental animal and the human being from that observed in hemolytic streptococcal infections.

A third type of host response has been observed in mice infected with *Cl. welchii* and treated with sulfanilamide. It was found in these experiments that without pretreatment of the organisms, but with the mice treated thirty minutes before being infected, the bacteriostatic effects of the drug are immediately evident. There is no lag period in the action of the drug in this type of infection. It is also of interest to observe that in the beginning phagocytosis is equal in both the control mice and the treated mice, but that, as time goes on, less phagocytosis is noted in the treated mice— obviously because there are fewer bacilli to be engulfed, owing to the inhibitory action of the drug upon the reproduction of the microörganisms. This, therefore, represents a host response in which no bar to phagocytosis exists in either the treated or control animals, and which clearly demonstrates the bacteriostatic activities of the drug in vivo.

It is evident from the experiments just outlined that the nature of the host response is of importance if a clear picture of the mechanism of action of sulfanilamide and its derivatives in the control of infections is to be obtained. Thus far we have been able to demonstrate two main types of host response. In the first, phagocytosis seems to have an important function in finally ridding the animal of the infectious agent, whereas specific antibody production either does not occur or is of minor importance. In the second type of host response, primary phagocytosis is slight, and the drug exercises merely an inhibitory effect upon the infectious agent until the naturally developing specific immune bodies are able to cope with the infection. A third type of host response may exist in which, though phagocytosis is very important, the primary factor in recovery seems to be the immediate bacteriostatic effects of the drug upon the invading microörganisms.

SUMMARY AND CONCLUSIONS

It seems quite probable from the evidence now available that the chemotherapeutic activity of $N=N$ or NH-R derivatives of sulfanilamide results from the breakdown to the parent compound in the tissues of the infected host. In general the SO_2NH-R linkage is a firm one. Effective sulfonamide compounds act as bacteriostatic and, under certain conditions, as bactericidal agents against susceptible bacteria. Whether or not sulfanilamide or its derivatives have the power of inactivating bacterial toxins is still a matter of dispute. At the present time it has been definitely shown that under certain conditions para amino benzoic acid and methionine can neutralize the bacteriostatic effects of sulfanilamide. It has been suggested that para amino benzoic acid exerts its neutralizing influence as the result of its being in competition with sulfanilamide for a place in certain enzyme systems of susceptible bacteria. The mechanism by which methionine neutralizes sulfanilamide is unknown. It is important to recognize the varied host response to infections if a complete picture of the mode of action of these drugs is to be obtained.

For References see p. 303.

X

SOME SCIENTIFIC ASPECTS OF THE SYNTHETIC RUBBER PROBLEM

By H. MARK

Polytechnic Institute of Brooklyn

INTRODUCTION

DURING the last fifteen years a new branch of organic chemistry has been started and gradually developed, the chemistry of high polymers. The natural products belonging to this class of substances, for example, cellulose, starch, proteins, chitin, rubber, etc., have been known for a long time, but it was only recently that successful attempts were made to elucidate their molecular structure and to realize their common fundamental building principle. Synthetic products of resinous character built up from small molecules, such as formaldehyde, ethyleneoxide, vinylchloride, and styrene, have also been known for some time, but again their molecular structure and their fundamental relationship with the natural high polymers were not known until about ten or fifteen years ago.

However, through the efforts of many prominent investigators, among whom it seems to be fair to mention particularly W. T. Astbury [2], W. H. Carothers [10], K. Freudenberg [19], W. N. Haworth [33], H. Hibbert [36], J. W. Hill [37], P. Karrer [39], E. O. Kraemer [43] [44], C. S. Marvel [54] [55], K. H. Meyer [57] [58], H. Staudinger [72], and G. S. Whitby [81] new experimental methods for the investigation of high polymers have been developed, and their application has led to a general structural picture of these materials. This concept will certainly be subject to many further improvements and modifications, but it seems fundamentally sound, and it is improbable that it will have to be changed radically in future.

Thus, it appears fair to say that we have reasonably well-founded ideas concerning the molecular structure of high polymers. A brief presentation of those ideas will be given in Section 2 of this discussion.

The next important step was to attempt to understand the physical and chemical properties of high polymers, which result from their molecular structure and are responsible for the considerable interest that industry and the public show in the subject. Let us briefly consider some of these properties:

Extreme tenacity (up to nearly 8 grams per denier)* combined with toughness and rigidity (modulus of elasticity up to 5×10^{11} dynes per sq. cm.) † is found in many cases, as in cellulose (flax, hemp), proteins (silk), polyamides (nylon), polyvinyl derivatives (vinyon, saran), etc. [3] [10] [23] [24] [28] [58].

Long-range reversible elasticity (up to 1,200 per cent elongation) combined with high ultimate strength (up to 5 grams per denier) and high chemical resistance against acids and alkalis is encountered in rubber, polychloroprene (neoprene), polybutadiene, and its copolymers (buna S, buna N, butyl-rubber) [1] [4] [9] [20] [29] [52] [76] [80].

Outstanding *electrical properties* combined with extreme

* Gram per denier is the common unit to measure the strength of textile fibers and yarns. One gram is the weight of one cubic cm. of water at 15° C.; one denier is the cross section of a fiber, of which 9,000 m. weigh one gram. Most fibers (with the exception of inorganic materials, such as silicate glass fibers or metal wires) have densities between 1.1 (polyethylene) and 1.6 (polyvinylidene chloride). The majority of the technical fibers (cotton, rayon, silk, nylon, wool) have densities between 1.3 and 1.5. In these latter cases the diameter of a cylindrical filament having one denier cross section is 10.4 microns and 9.7 microns, respectively.

† The modulus of elasticity is the force necessary to produce initial elongation; it is given by the initial slope of the stress-strain curve and is measured in dynes per sq. cm., kg. per sq. mm., or lbs. per sq. in. In this case (5×10^{11} dynes per sq. cm.) the material has a modulus of 5,000 kg. per sq. mm. or 780,000 lbs. per sq. in.

chemical resistivity and in cases with high temperature stability are exhibited by polyethylene (polythene), polystyrene, polyphenol formaldehyde (bakelite), polyglycerol phtalate (glyptals), and many others [8] [58].

Excellent *molding properties* combined with transparency, chemical resistivity, and high impact strength are characteristic of many high polymers, such as nitrocellulose, cellulose acetate, polystyrene, polyacrylic derivatives (lucite, plexiglass), polyvinyl derivatives (vinylites, koroseal), etc.

This list of examples illustrating the attractive chemical and physical properties of high polymers could be greatly extended, but for the purpose of this article consideration may be limited to the cases mentioned above.

It would be an exaggeration to pretend that we know *all* the qualities that result from the molecular structure of these substances, or that we can establish a numerical relationship between structure and properties. However, it can be said that a *quantitative* relationship has been established in *some* particularly important cases and that a general *qualitative* correlation to the structure can be given for most of the physical and chemical properties. The third section of this article will attempt to sketch this relationship between fundamental molecular structure and empirical chemical and physical properties in some representative cases.

The establishment of the molecular structure seems to be of considerable importance, because it permits the designing of high polymers having certain desired properties without being forced to copy any substance existing in nature that has been used hitherto for technical purposes. The deeper scientific understanding of how structure determines properties enables us to quit copying natural materials slavishly and without imagination. Instead, it allows us to use the acquired fundamental knowledge and to create new types of materials with properties, never before obtained—properties, which for certain given purposes excel considerably the qualities of all natural materials.

Chemistry has repeatedly succeeded in accomplishing a similar development. It will be remembered that the first synthetic dyestuffs, drugs, and alloys were close analogies to those previously found in nature. Therefore, the new synthetic products were not notably superior to the natural products; they were just copies. Later, however, as the fundamental knowledge of the connections between structure and properties was built up, it became possible to design and synthesize alloys, dyestuffs, and drugs having qualities far superior to those of the natural products. This development, of course, took some time and required a considerable amount of fundamental and applied research work.

There can be little doubt that in the case of high polymers we are facing a similar situation. At present, when we are just beginning to understand the molecular structure of these materials and its connection with their properties, chemists have still to move cautiously and in some association with the natural models. But there is already proof of the fact that one can build up synthetic high polymers which have no chemical similarity whatsoever with any natural product and yet exhibit extremely interesting and important physical and chemical properties. It is the writer's belief that our ever-growing fundamental knowledge will enable chemists increasingly to use their imagination and that soon they will *design synthetic polymers for special uses far superior to any natural product previously employed for the same purpose.*

After this short general introduction we shall proceed to describe the molecular structure of high polymers and to connect it with their chemical and physical properties.

SOME FEATURES OF THE STRUCTURE OF HIGH POLYMERS

(a) *Average Molecular Weight and Polymerization Degree*

The outstanding factor of high polymers is that they are built up by *very large molecules*. The molecular weight* of normal organic substances is of the order of magnitude around several hundreds. Table I shows a few examples of

TABLE I

Molecular Weights of Some Normal Organic Chemical Substances.

Substance	Molecular weight $0 = 16.0000$
Alcohol	46
Acetic acid	60
Aniline	93
Naphthalene	128
Aspirin	202
Cane sugar	342
Indanthrene blue	410

well-known organic substances, with molecular weights ranging from 46 to 410. There are a few other more complex substances, such as azodyestuffs, tanning agents, etc., with molecular weights up to 1,000, but the large majority of normal organic compounds stay below 500 or 600.

In contrast, high polymers have molecular weights ranging from twenty thousand to several hundred thousand and, in some cases, up to a million. This can be considered as an established fact today, but it was not settled for several years until all differences in opinion were overcome and all doubts about the reliability of the figures removed [13] [17] [18] [25] [38] [41] [42] [45]. Fortunately, there are several methods to

* This is the figure which indicates how many times the molecule under consideration is heavier than a hydrogen atom. (To be exact, the weight of H is not unity but 1.0078.) It characterizes the relative weight of those smallest particles of the sample, which are held together by primary bonds and which in the vapor phase or in diluted solution act as kinetic units.

measure or at least to estimate the molecular weight of high polymers.

One of them is the determination of the *osmotic pressure* of a high polymer in very diluted solution, which leads, with the aid of Van't Hoff's formula, directly to the molecular weight of the kinetic unit. If one dissolves at room temperature one gram of the high polymer under consideration in one liter of the solvent (say, water or toluene) and measures the osmotic pressures by the height h of a column of the solvent in millimeters, then the molecular weight M of the material is given by the formula.*

$$M = \frac{240,000}{h} \tag{1}$$

Thus a material, such as cellulose acetate with a molecular weight of 24,000 produces a solvent column of 10 mm. or 1 cm., which can be easily measured. On the other hand, a high polymer like native cotton, with a molecular weight of 500,000, gives a pressure difference of less than 0.5 mm., which is difficult to measure by this method [26] [50] [58].

Another very important method for determining the molecular weight of high polymers is the *ultracentrifuge* of Svedberg [74]. With its aid the diluted solution of a high polymer is subjected to a strong centrifugal field (up to one million times earth gravity) and the rate and the equilibrium of sedimentation are observed. Knowing the density of the dry polymer and of the solvent, one can calculate the molecular weight of the former. This method is effective even with the highest molecular weights and has been used extensively for studies on all important high polymers; it is very reliable but expensive [43] [50] [58].

In many instances it has been found that the large mole-

* This formula is only an approximation, but is sufficiently correct as long as the density of the solvent is not too far from 1.

cules of a high polymer are straight chains in which all links are identical. For example, cellulose is built up by the association of glucose groups, rubber by isoprene residues, nylon by adipic acid and hexamethylenediamine units, etc. In all these examples, the groups at one or both ends of the chains have a different chemical structure from the groups in the middle of the chain. Thus each cellulose chain has a potential aldehyde group (—COH), each rubber chain has a double bond ($H_2C=CH$—) on one end, whereas each nylon chain has either a carboxyl (—COOH) or an amino (—NH_2) group on each end. These *functional groups* can often be determined by chemical means. Knowing their number n in a given amount, say in one gram, of the high polymer under consideration and knowing the molecular weight M_0 of the monomonic unit, one can determine the molecular weight M of the polymer with the aid of the formula

$$M = \frac{A}{n} M_0 \tag{2}$$

where A is Avogadro's number equaling 6×10^{23}.

The factor $\frac{A}{n}$ indicates how many monomers are linked together in one long molecular chain; it is usually called the degree of polymerization (DP) or the polymerization degree (P). It is very conveniently used in comparing different high polymers, such as rubber and cellulose, or neoprene and saran, because the investigator is frequently more interested in the comparative length of the chains than he is in their comparative weight.

Another method which allows estimating the molecular weight of high polymers in a very simple way was discovered by Staudinger [72] and later improved by Fuller [24], Fuoss [25], Hibbert [36], Huggins [38], Kraemer [43] [44], Kuhn [45],

Lauffer [47], Meyer [58], Schulz [69], Simha [70], Straus and Levy [73]. It consists in measuring the *viscosity, η_c, of a solution* of a high polymer having a very low concentration c (say one gram per liter). One then subtracts the viscosity η_0 of the solvent, and gets $\eta_c - \eta_0$, which is the viscosity increase of the system due to the presence of the dissolved high polymer. Finally, one measures the viscosity increase in terms of η_0 and obtains the relative increase of viscosity of the solvent produced by the addition of the high polymer. This quantity $\dfrac{\eta_c - \eta_0}{\eta_0}$ has been defined by Staudinger as *specific viscosity* [72] and is usually denoted by η_{sp}. It has been found experimentally, and it has also been derived theoretically [50], [70], that this specific viscosity is related, under certain restricting conditions, to the molecular weight M of the polymer by an equation of the formula

$$\eta_{sp} = a + \beta M \tag{3}$$

a and β are constants characteristic for each pair of high polymers and solvent and vary but little with other experimental parameters, such as temperature, rate of flow, etc. If they are once determined for a given system, equation [3] allows a convenient though not very accurate determination of M. The viscosity method is widely used to get a quick first idea of the polymerization degree of a material and to follow it through any kind of technical procedure.

Several hundred high polymers of various structures have been investigated with the methods just described, and the results of the different methods have checked fairly satisfactorily. It is not that a precision agreement of the polymerization degrees as determined by ultracentrifuge, osmotic pressure, end group titration, and viscosity is obtained, but, under proper precautions, one always gets the same order of magnitude. This shows that these figures have physical significance and can be used as a sound basis for further investigations. Before taking the next step in the characterization of high polymers, it may be appropriate to introduce Table II, which contains some numerical values concerning the molecular weights of various high polymers.

TABLE II

Molecular Weights and Polymerization Degrees of Some High Polymers.

Material investigated	Molecular weight	Polymerization degree
Native cellulose in cotton, ramie, or wood	300,000–500,000	2,000–3,000
Cellulose in bleached cotton linters	150,000–230,000	1,000–1,500
Cellulose in purified wood pulp	120,000–200,000	800–1,200
Regenerated cellulose in rayon	75,000–100,000	500– 600
Regenerated cellulose in staple fiber	60,000– 75,000	400– 500
Regenerated cellulose in cellophane	50,000– 60,000	300– 400
Native rubber in Hevea latex	140,000–210,000	2,000–3,000
Rubber after being milled in air	55,000– 70,000	800–1,000
Nitrocellulose used for molding	400,000–700,000	1,500–2,500
Nitrocellulose used for extrusion	150,000–300,000	600–1,200
Nitrocellulose used for coatings	50,000–100,000	200– 400
Polystyrene for plate casting	250,000–400,000	2,500–4,000
Polystyrene for injection molding	120,000–180,000	1,200–1,800
Polystyrene for coatings	80,000–120,000	800–1,200
Polyvinyl chloride (koroseal)	250,000	3,000
Polyisobutylene (vistanex)	120,000–200,000	2,000–3,000
Polyhexa methylene adipamate (nylon)	16,000– 32,000	150– 300

The first column of Table II contains the high polymer under consideration, together with a few remarks concerning its history, the second column shows the limits of the molecular weight as they have been determined with the methods described above, and, finally, the third contains the corresponding limits for the polymerization degree. Its figures are obtained from those of the second column by dividing them by the molecular weight of the monomer.

Table II shows, for instance, that the cellulose in native cotton, rayon, or wood has a polymerization degree of about

2,000 to 3,000; similar figures have been found for native rubber and for various synthetic polymers, such as polyiso-butylene, polystyrene, and polyvinyl chloride. In polystyrene Alfrey has even succeeded in obtaining polymerization degrees above 10,000, and with polyisobutylene values up to 7,000 have been reported by Frolich, Muller, Otto, Sparks, and Thomas [76]. It seems that samples of even higher degrees of polymerization can be obtained by proper procedures.

However, for many technical purposes one degrades the original material and stabilizes its polymerization degree at some lower level. Experience has shown that this method facilitates, quite definitely, the processing of mixtures, compounds, or solutions of most high polymers, without influencing too much certain mechanical properties of the samples. Thus it can be seen from Table II that for the convenience of spinning or casting solutions of cellulose or its derivatives, the manufacturing process is initiated with a material such as bleached cotton linters or purified wood pulp, both of which have polymerization degrees around 1,000. Later the chain length is reduced still further by degrading the material in the form of sodiumcellulose in the presence of air (aging of alkalicellulose). The cellulose chains in the final products—rayon, staple fiber, cellophane —have an average length of only 300 to 600 glucose units, a polymerization degree which corresponds to a molecular weight as high as 50,000 to 100,000.

Similarly native rubber is degraded to a polymerization degree below 1,000 by milling it in the presence of oxygen in order to facilitate the incorporation of fillers, plasticizers, and vulcanization ingredients.

With synthetic polymers it is sometimes possible to control the polymerization process in such a way that one can at least approximately predetermine the polymerization degree of the resulting product. If this is the case, different types of the same polymer are produced for different industrial purposes, such as for coating, extrusion, injection-molding, etc. Table II shows, as examples, nitrocellulose and polystyrene.

(b) *The Chain-Length Distribution Curve*

The next step in the characterization of a high polymer is based on the fact that all natural and synthetic polymers are heterogeneous in respect to the lengths of the chains which they contain. Carothers [10], Meyer [58], and Staudinger [72] have pointed out that every sample must be considered as being a mixture of chains having different degrees of polymerization, so that the figures of Table II can only be considered as *average values*. In the last years this heterogeneity of high polymers has been very intensely studied by Flory [18], Fuoss [26], Harris [31], Kemp [41] [42], Kraemer [44], Ott [62], Peters [42], Schieber [68], Schulz [69], Spurlin [71], Sookne [31], Simha [70], and others. Various methods of fractionation have been worked out for the experimental determination of the chain-length distribution and have been applied in several cases.

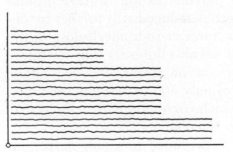

FIG. 98. Sketch of a chain-length distribution curve in its integral step form.

The results of such fractionation experiments can be conveniently represented by a *chain-length distribution curve,* in which the number of chains having a polymerization degree between P and $P + dP$ is plotted against P. Such a *differential distribution curve* can be worked out if we have a method for removing all molecules of a given length from the sample. We first start to remove the longest chains and consider them to be laid parallel to each other in a Carthesian coördinate system, as shown in Figure 98. In drawing the figure it was assumed that there are four chains of this largest length present; in reality their number will be of the order of magnitude of 10^{17} or 10^{18} per gram of the polymer. Pulling out the chains of the next shorter length and adding them to the longer ones, we obtain another step in our curve. The more chains of this kind present, the steeper the step will be. Let us assume there are eight chains of this length. Then we remove four chains of the next shorter length, and finally two of the shortest length represented in the sample. The step curve obtained by this procedure represents the number of chains on the ordinate against their length on the abscissae. The length l is proportional to the polymerization degree P. The next task is to convert the broken curve of Figure 98 into a continuous line by smoothing out the steps. This interpolation will obviously be better the closer and m o r e frequent the steps are. A good fractionation requires, therefore, a large number of fractions. Figure 99 shows the result of such a smoothing out of the step curve of Figure 98. It gives n as a function of l or P. What is wanted, however, is the number of chains belonging to a given interval dP. Hence it is necessary to differentiate the curve of Figure 99. Where its slope is gentle we have only few chains, where it is steep we have a larger number

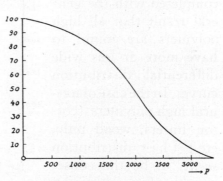

Fig. 99. Step curve of Fig. 98 interpolated into a smooth integral distribution curve.

of them. This can be immediately seen from the step curve in Figure 98.

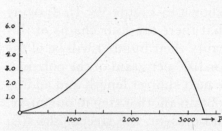

FIG. 100. Differential distribution curve corresponding to the integral curve of Fig. 99.

The result of differentiation of the curve in Figure 99 is represented in Figure 100; it gives the usual type of a differential distribution curve which reflects in a fairly convenient way the heterogeneity of the given material. The curve in Figure 100, for example, shows that the most frequent polymerization degree in the sample is around $P = 2,000$ and that a rather wide range of chain lengths is covered by the molecules of the material.

In the last few years a fairly large number of fractionation experiments have been completed with the general result that all high polymers are found to have more or less wide differential distribution curves. In the case of natural high polymers (cotton linters, wood pulp, etc.) this distribution seems to be the consequence of a certain amount of degradation which takes place during the purification of the

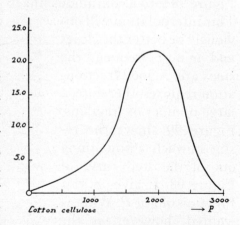

FIG. 101a. Experimental differential distribution curve of cellulose in cotton linters.

material in the manufacturing process. Figure 101 shows a few differential chain-length distribution curves of cellulose and cellulose acetate as they have been determined experimentally during the last years [6] [31] [51] [53] [61] [66] [68] [71] [73]. They are all comparatively wide, showing that these materials are very far from being homogeneous.

In the synthetic polymers, on the other hand, the chain-length distribution appears as a consequence of the different elementary steps—activation, propagation, termination, chain transfer, and branching—which

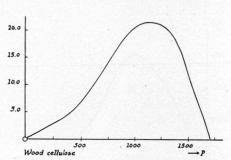

Fig. 101b. Experimental differential distribution curve of cellulose in wood pulp.

coöperate during a polymerization reaction. Figure 102 shows a few examples of experimentally determined chain-length distribution curves of polyisobutylene and polystyrene. Again it can be seen that the curves cover a considerable range of chain lengths, and represent a rather high degree of heterogeneity.

From an examination of Figures 101 and 102 it becomes obvious that the characterization of a high polymer by its molecular weight or polymerization degree is a rather crude oversimplification. There exists no such quantity

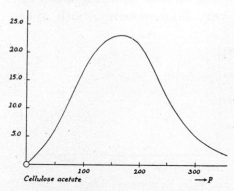

Fig. 101c. Experimental differential distribution curve for a cellulose acetate.

for the whole sample. Apparently the appropriate thing to do is to take the distribution curve, compute the average value, and put it forward as the *average polymerization degree* of the material. In doing so, one must keep in mind the fact that different average values can be obtained from distribution curves as shown in Figures 101 and 102. Flory [18], Kraemer [44], Schulz [69], and Simha [70] have investigated this problem very thoroughly, with the result that one has mainly to deal with two types of averages, namely, (a) *t h e number average polymerization degree* which is experimentally obtained by end-group titration and osmotic measurements, and (b) the *weight average polymerization degree* which is the result of viscosity or sedimentation experiments. If a sample is very homogeneous, both averages converge to the same value; if the material has a distribution curve as shown in Figures 101 or 102, the weight average is about twice the number average. This prediction has been confirmed experimentally in several instances.

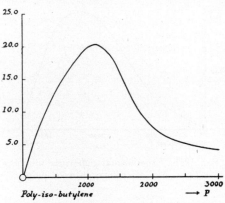

Fig. 102a. Experimental differential distribution curve of polyisobutylene.

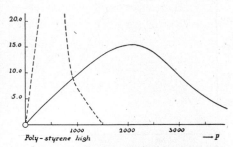

Fig. 102b. Experimental differential distribution curve of polystyrene (high).

(c) *Branching and Cross Linking*

In the discussion thus far we have attempted to characterize the molecules of a given high polymer in respect to their average size and their size distribution, always assuming that they were all straight chains. It appears that this condition is true in certain substances, such as cellulose, rubber, gutta, nylon, silk, etc., but not always. There are experimental and theoretical reasons to believe that in other polymers, such as glyptals, polystyrene, polyvinyl chloride, etc., certain types of branching reactions take place, which result in molecules of rather complicated shape.

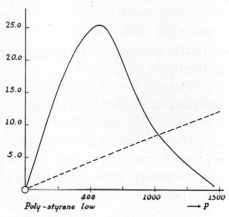

Fig. 102c. Experimental differential distribution curve of polystyrene (low).

If one condenses glycol with adipic acid, it is obvious that the progressing esterification of the hydroxyl and carboxyl groups can only lead to straight chains according to the formula

$$HOCH_2 - CH_2OH + HOOC(CH_2)_4COOH \rightarrow$$
$$HOCH_2 - CH_2OOC(CH_2)_4COOH$$

As soon, however, as glycerol is used instead of glycol, one can get—and actually does get—branching. This can be expressed by the following scheme:

$$HOCH_2 - CHOH - CH_2OH + 2 HOOC(CH_2)_4COOH \rightarrow$$
$$HOCH_2 - CHCH_2 OOC(CH_2)_4 COOH$$
$$\diagdown$$
$$O - OC(CH_2)_4COOH$$

The secondary hydroxyl group in each glycerol molecule is a possible place to start a branch, and as the reaction proceeds a very complicated three-dimensional network will have been built up which is highly resistant to solvents and heat. Polycondensation reactions, in which more than bifunctional molecules are involved, lead, therefore, to *thermosetting* materials such as phenol formaldehyde, urea formaldehyde, or glyptal.

Another type of branching takes place during the polymerization of vinyl derivations. To the best of our present knowledge, the formation of the long molecules is performed by a *chain reaction* during which an *activated molecule* having the character of a free radical grows into a chain by adding monomer after monomer. This can be represented by the scheme

(a) Activation:
catalyst + monomer → active radical
$$K + CH_2 = CHX \rightarrow KCH_2 - CHX -$$

(b) Propagation:
active radical + monomer → growing chain
$$KCH_2 - CHX - + CH_2 = CHX \rightarrow$$
$$KCH_2 - CHX - CH_2 - CHX -$$

The process (b) has a low activation energy ($E \frown 5,000$ cals. per mole) and is, therefore, repeated frequently (about 1,000 times) in a very short period (about .01 second), so that the chain grows to its full length (P around 1,000) within a comparatively short time.

If only processes of the type (a) and (b) would operate, the result of such a polymerization reaction would be straight chains of virtually infinite length. However, in any actual case, at least two other processes interfere. One of them *terminates* the growing chains according to the following formula:

(c) Termination:
   growing chain + growing chain →
                              stabilized (terminated) chain
   $KCH_2 — CHX — + — HXC — CH_2K →$
                      $KCH_2 — CHX — CHX — CH_2K$

The other gives rise to *branching* of the chains. It can be represented by the following scheme:

(d) Branching:
   growing chain + growing chain →
                              terminated chain + branching chain
   $KCH_2 — CHX — + — HXC — CH_2K →$
                      $KCH_2 — CH_2X + > XC — CH_2K$

During such a process the free valence at the end of one growing chain is transferred to the other chain with the result that one chain is stabilized whereas the other has two free valencies and hence the possibility of continuing its propagation along two branches.

The frequency with which such a *transfer of the free valence* occurs depends to a large extent upon the nature of the substituent X and of temperature. Some polyvinyl derivatives seem to exhibit more tendency to branch than do others. There is, however, no definite and reliable criterion available as yet for the exact amount of branching and for a more detailed description of the branched chains. Boyer [7], Flory [18], Schulz [69], and others [51] have developed experimental methods to determine the amount of branching in a given case and have also worked out equations which tie branching into the general schedule of polymerization reactions.

Highly branched chains have a shape approaching that of a spherical or nearly spherical particle; they differ from straight chains in their flow properties and in the distribution curve.

The type of branching just discussed is characterized by the fact that propagation and branching are going on simultaneously; that is, while the chains are growing, they are developing branches. There exists, however, a very important second way to produce more dimensional networks of long-chain molecules, namely, *cross linking*.

This process takes place when a polymer, which consists already of long chains, is treated in such a way that comparatively short cross links are developed between the chains. The classical case of a cross-linking reaction is found in the vulcanization of rubber. The chains of rubber contain double bonds, which add sulfur. The additional product is capable of reacting with another double bond which produces two sulfur bridges between two chain molecules.*

As long as the cross bonds are not too frequent, say one cross link on a hundred straight links (which corresponds to about 1 per cent sulfur by weight), the sample retains its softness and flexibility and remains thermoplastic. This type of moderate cross linking is practically identical with a certain amount of branching as described above.

However, if the cross bonds become frequent (one after each ten straight bonds) the structure is very much stiffened and a hard, thermostable substance is obtained, which is insoluble, does not swell, and exhibits all the characteristics of a three-dimensional tight network.

With this brief discussion of branching and cross linking, it may be appropriate to close the *geometrical* characterization of the molecules of a high polymer. Having dealt with their average size, their size distribution, and their shape, we shall now proceed to the description of the *dynamical* circumstances, particularly the *forces* which act between the long chains (straight or branched) and their effects on the structure of high polymers.

* For further information, see chap. V in the fundamental book of J. T. Blake and C. C. Davis, *Rubber Chemistry* (New York, 1940).

(d) *Intermolecular Forces in High Polymers*

Table II and Figures 101 and 102 show that most high polymers have a similar average degree of polymerization and also have distribution curves that do not deviate from each other very appreciably. Nevertheless, polyisobutylene, polyvinyl acetate, and polyvinylidene chloride having similar average polymerization degrees and similar distribution curves behave very differently. The first material is a typical rubber, the second shows all properties of a plastic, whereas the third is a characteristic fiber-forming high polymer. It seems that this difference in appearance and behavior of these substances can be reasonably explained as being caused by the different forces which act between the long-chain molecules and tend to bring those chains into a certain state of organization.

Early work of Astbury [2], Herzog [35], Katz [40], Polany [64], Scherrer [67], Weissenberg [50] [58], and others [57] has shown that many high polymers show distinct X-ray patterns which reveal the presence of a certain amount of crystalline material. Subsequent investigations of Baker [3], Clark [11], Field [15], Fuller [21] [22], Gehman [27], Hauser [32], Hengstenberg [57], Sisson [58], Susich [58], and others allow us to draw a more detailed picture of the supermolecular structure of high polymers.

Certain areas of a given sample have a high degree of internal geometrical organization and exhibit certain properties which are commonly found with crystals. One usually refers to them as *crystallites,* or *micells*. They diffract X rays of medium wave length in such a way that regular fiber patterns of a certain intensity and sharpness are produced. They exhibit birefringence and show distinct anisotropy in some physical and chemical properties. On the contrary, these crystallized areas are in certain respects unlike the crystals of normal organic substances. They do not have well-defined and plane boundaries and do not exhibit sharp symmetrical edges. Their size seems to vary widely; in some substances, such as proteins or vinylcopolymers, they can be very small, though normally they are rod- or ribbon-like and have dimensions between 50 and 10,000 Å.U.* In other instances, it has been observed that they can grow to comparatively large homogeneous units of dimensions up to 10^6 Å.U.

It seems evident that these crystallites of a high polymer should be compared not so much with the completely shaped and altogether independent single individuals of a crystal sugar powder as with the grains of a polycrystalline metal wire or sheet. These grains also show many typical properties of normal crystals (X-ray pattern, birefringence, anisotropy) but, on the other hand, do not have plane boundaries and sharp edges. It may be worthwhile to point out that, in general, the experimental and theoretical investigations of organic high polymers can use the methods developed for and applied in the study of metals very advantageously. We are out to build up a metallography of organic chemical systems.

With reference to cellulose crystallites, or rubber micells, we shall, therefore, understand small areas of somewhat indefinite size and shape, inside of which the monomeric units are arranged in a three-dimensional periodic pattern.

There are, however, in every sample of a high polymer also certain portions which are not crystallized. These are usually referred to as the *amorphous, disordered, intermicellar,* or *glassy* fractions. Several investigators, particularly Baker [3], Clark [11], Fuller [23], Harris [31], Hermans [34], Kratky [50], Nickerson [60], Pape [23], and Purves [65] have used different methods to get information about these con-

---

* Because they are dealing with such extremely small distances physicists commonly measure them in Ångstrom units (Å. U.), each of which is equal to $\frac{1}{100}$ millionth of a centimeter or $\frac{1}{254}$ millionth of an inch.

stituents of a high polymer. It seems that they contain the chains in a less perfect arrangement, due to the fact, for instance, that some irregularity has prevented them from reaching the proper equilibrium positions of the crystallized state. It is believed that one and the same chain can go through a crystalline area, enter an amorphous portion, go right through it, and enter another crystallite. This assumption leads to the conclusion that there is no sharp boundary between the crystallized and disordered areas, but that the chains of a certain crystal get somehow in disorder, degenerate into fringes according to Gerngross, Hermann, and Abitz [58], and, finally, reach a completely disordered arrangement. Hence it may be appropriate not to make a sharp distinction between crystallized and amorphous, but to consider *various degrees of disorder,* just as one has observed different crystallized modifications. Baker, Fuller, and Pape [3] have proposed to consider *mesomorphous phases* in quenched polyamides, and H. S. Taylor [75] has repeatedly emphasized that chains with regularly distributed centers of attraction are unlikely to curl up in a completely irregular way.

There seem to be even different degrees of randomness in a substance like rubber as is indicated by its thermal properties, particularly by the existence of a second-order transition point around $-80°$ C., which was established by careful measurements of Bekkedahl and Wood [4] [80]. Transition points of higher order seem to be a rather general feature in high polymers with chains of a certain internal flexibility or foldability, such as polystyrene, polyisobutylene, and polyacrylates. Theoretical considerations relative to a certain degree of regular folding in amorphous rubber were carried out several years ago by Kirchhoff, Fikentscher [16], and others [57] [58], and were later definitely improved by E. Mack [49], who even based on them a theory of the elastic properties of rubber.

Polystyrene of polymerization degrees between 1,000 and 2,000 has not yet been forced into a definite crystalline structure by any mechanical or thermal pretreatment, but it shows a distinct transition point around 80°C. and, according to experiments of D. Whyte [82], exhibits an amorphous X-ray diagram in which sharpness and intensity distribution of the diffuse halo can be affected by appropriate pretreatments.

All this shows that even in chain-like (or slightly branched) hydrocarbons, where the intermolecular forces are weak and geometrically diffuse, various degrees of disorder exist and contribute to the mechanical behavior of the material.

The tendency for a certain regularity in the curled-up state seems to be distinctly more pronounced if groups with attractive forces, such as permanent dipoles, easily polarizable bonds, or hydrogen-bonding groups, are regularly distributed along the chain. Proteins are a very good example of such systems. Astbury first brought attention to the fact that α- and β-keratin are two modifications of the same chain which is differently folded in the two types. According to Bernal [5], Fankuchen [14], Harris [31], Huggins [38], Langmuir [46], Pauling [63], and Wrinch [83], it seems evident that protein-type chains have a large variety of possibilities to fold up into regular, or crystallized, arrangements. It appears reasonable to assume that this tendency also persists if the areas of geometrical order become very small, so that under all conditions a certain regularity of the curled-up state is maintained in very small areas.

The X-ray diagrams of proteins indicate that those materials are far from being completely crystallized. On the contrary, the few and indistinct spots, which have been used as a basis for establishing the structure of wool or muscle, are surrounded by a very distinct general scattering indicating a large amount of disordered material in the sample. The intensity characteristics of this diffuse background deviate quite markedly from the normal aspect of a liquid diagram, and show that the chemical nature of the material does not allow a completely randomized arrangement of the chain segments in small volumes.

Another indication for a certain structure of the disordered or amorphous portions has been put forward recently by the study of polyamides. Baker, Fuller, and Pape [3] have investigated the crystallization of polyamides under different experimental conditions. H. S. Taylor [75] has emphasized that certain mechanical properties of polyamides can be well understood if one assumes a regular folding of the chains in the quenched state.

In the sense of these considerations, cold drawing can be visualized as converting internal crystallization (regular curling up of the different individual chains) into external crystallization (parallelization of straightened-out chains). The curled-up state of a single isolated chain represents a minimum of its free energy and, hence, under given conditions, is a stable arrangement. If one wants to extend such a chain, it is first necessary to overcome the hydrogen bonds between its segments and hence a certain force is needed to accomplish the elongation. It is true that one first brings the chain in a more probable position, but the small gain in randomness (entropy) does not count in comparison with the considerable loss in potential energy. Later, when the most probable shape of the chain is passed, the extending force has to work mainly against bringing the chain in less and less probable positions, because after a certain straightening out has taken place the attraction centers are getting out of range and the internal cohesion decreases rapidly.

If, however, we do not have a single chain, but a whole entangled multitude of them (and this is always the case in reality), another effect interferes. As soon as the chains are slightly disentangled, and the different segments are removed from their equilibrium positions corresponding to the folded-up state, mutual attraction of segments belonging to different chains will become appreciable. This mutual attraction helps to straighten the chains and to produce their complete parallelization. During this stage, the external force is greatly assisted by the molecular attraction between different chains, a fact which can be observed very distinctly during the drawing of many high polymers, during the extension of rubber [1] [52] and very clearly during the spontaneous elongation of long-chain compounds. The final state of this procedure is complete mutual crystallization of the chains, which means the formation of a highly crystallized and oriented sample. As Alfrey [1] has pointed out, however, such an extreme state can never be reached in reality, due to the fact that crystallization does not start in one single point, but at many different spots all over the sample. The growing crystals interfere with each other in such a way that a certain amount of the material always remains in the disordered state, even if all possible measures have been taken to achieve the highest degree of regularity.

This picture of the conversion of folded-up chains having a certain degree of internal regularity into straightened-out chains having a higher degree of mutual geometrical organization seems to be one molecular mechanism which accompanies the mechanical deformation of a long-chain polymer.

Whether the free energy has its absolute minimum in the initial state (curled-up chains) or in the final arrangement of the system (mutual crystallization of the chains) depends upon the molecular attraction between the chains, upon their geometrical fitting into the crystal lattice, upon temperature and other external forces. If the *molecular attraction* is *small*, and the *chains fit badly into a lattice*, then at a given temperature and stress the material will always have the tendency to *return* to its original state. *Such conditions are typical for rubber.*

On the other hand, if the *forces* are *strong,* and the fine structure of the chains provides for *easy fitting into a lattice,* a state of high external crystallinity is favored, and the material is a typical *fiber.*

In intermediate cases, in which the forces are *moderate* and the geometry of the chains is *moderately favorable for crystallization,* the behavior of the material will greatly depend upon external conditions, such as temperature and mechanical forces. Such systems are typical *plastics.*

These short qualitative considerations show that rubbers, plastics, and fibers are not intrinsically different materials. Their differences are much more matters of degree produced by the way in which the intermolecular forces between the long chains and their general tendency for curling and folding coöperate in forming a certain mixture of crystallized and disordered portions in the sample.

ASSOCIATION BETWEEN SOME PROPERTIES OF HIGH POLYMERS AND THEIR STRUCTURE

(a) *General Remarks*

After having reviewed briefly some of the most important structural features of high polymers, it may now be appropriate to consider how some of the most important properties of these substances are connected with their fundamental structure. Summarizing, first, the results of the last paragraph, we may state that the following are the main criteria for describing the structure of the high polymer:

1. The average molecular weight or chain length.
2. The chain-length distribution curve.
3. The amount of branching or cross linking.

4. The magnitude and geometrical distribution of the intermolecular forces.

We shall now consider the influence of each of these factors on the mechanical behavior of the material.

1. The connection between mechanical properties and average chain length has been frequently investigated. Early work in this direction was done by Carothers [10], Ohl [61], and Rocha [66]. More frequently this question was closely investigated by Harris [31], Sookne [31], Spurlin [71], and others [53] [73]. From the results it is clear that in order to obtain mechanical strength at all, the material must have a certain *minimum degree of polymerization*. This critical minimum value ranges between 40 and 80. It seems to be smallest in the case of nylon and largest in the case of polyhydrocarbons, such as polythene and polystyrene. As soon as this critical value of chain length is surpassed, the material starts to show mechanical strength, and the increase of tenacity is roughly proportional to the average degree of polymerization. Figure 103 shows this situation diagrammatically. The figure shows that up to the polymerization degree between 40 and 80 the tenacity is negligible and that it then increases proportionally to the chain length. The left border of the shaded area, which is denoted with little circles, holds for polyamides; while the right border, which is denoted with little crosses, holds for polyhydrocarbons. All other high polymers, such as cellulose esters, polyvinyl derivatives, etc., lie in between. The proportionality between mechanical strength and chain length holds until the polymerization degree is around 250. Then the curve flattens out gradually until, when it has reached a polymerization degree of about 600 or 700, the mechanical properties no longer depend to any appreciable extent upon the chain length.

The slope of the linear part of the curve in Figure 103 seems to depend not only upon the nature of the high polymer but also very considerably upon the type of spinning or casting which was used to prepare the sample. If one favors crystallization and orientation during spinning, molding, or casting, a higher level of mechanical strength is more quickly reached than when the material is left in a more disordered state. However, when once the spinning conditions are estab-

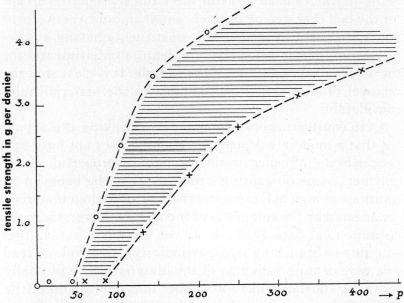

FIG. 103. Diagram connecting schematically tensile strength with average degree of polymerization.

lished, Figure 103 gives a fair picture of how the average chain length influences the mechanical properties of the material.

2. While the influence of the average polymerization degree on the mechanical strength is fairly well established and can with some justification be represented in a curve like Figure 103, the influence of the chain-length distribution is still an unsolved problem. Recently a few attempts

have been made by Harris [31], Schieber [68], Spurlin [71], Sookne [31], Simha [70], Straus and Levy [73], and others [51] to establish a connection between distribution curve and characteristic mechanical properties of high polymers. And it seems that the following can be put forward as the result of these investigations. There is no definite effect of the shape of the distribution curve on the mechanical properties except for the fact that a comparatively small amount (between 10 and 15 per cent by weight) of constituents having a polymerization degree below 150 are definitely detrimental for the mechanical properties of the sample. It is clear that the removal of such constituents improves the material quite considerably.

3. In considering branching and cross linking, it is apparent that a moderate degree of branching does not have any very definite influence on the mechanical properties of the polymer. Some observations indicate that the behavior of solutions of high polymers and the flow of molten materials are affected by the amount of branching. However, there are no numerical data available as yet for this effect. Larger amounts of branching and, particularly, cross linking lead to a very definite stiffening of the material and will finally convert a substance like soft rubber into a hard and brittle material. It may be added that even a small amount of cross linking decreases very considerably the solubility of the system and increases drastically its temperature resistance.

4. It seems that the magnitude and the geometrical arrangement of the intermolecular forces have great influence on the behavior of a high polymer and, as has already been pointed out, determine to a large extent whether a material behaves like a rubber, a plastic, or a fiber. As soon as a certain degree of polymerization is reached, which usually will be above 400 or 500, sufficient mechanical strength is provided to make the material useful. The more intimate prop-

erties, such as softness, flexibility, elastic behavior, etc., depend largely upon the magnitude and distribution of the intermolecular forces. If they are large and regularly distributed the material will exhibit a distinct tendency to crystallize and will, therefore, be of the fiber type. If the forces are small and (or) are irregularly distributed along the chain no crystallization tendency will prevail and the material will have the properties of rubber. Intermediate cases are characteristic for substances which we call plastics.

After this general discussion of the influence which the different features of the structure of a high polymer exert on its mechanical properties, it will be appropriate to discuss this question in more detail in connection with a few actual examples.

(b) Discussion of Some Special Cases

It will be appropriate to start with the description of the structure and properties of some vinyl polymers, because several of them have been studied quite extensively and, as a result, the fine structure of the crystallized parts of them is now known to a fair extent.

POLYETHYLENE

This material is prepared by polymerizing gaseous ethylene under pressure in the presence of certain catalysts. Polymerization degrees between 1,000 and 3,000 have been observed. The technical products are plastics, which melt comparatively sharply between 115° and 125°C. The polymerization process leads mainly to straight, normal, paraffin chains, but it seems that under the technical conditions a certain amount of branching and cross linking is not excluded [8] [21].

Upon mechanical deformation—rolling, or drawing—polyethylene crystallizes and furnishes fair X-ray patterns.

Their evaluation has to be credited mainly to Bunn who succeeded in determining the elementary cell, the space group, and in carrying out a complete Fourier analysis of the X-ray diagrams. The chains are arranged in an ortho-rhombic cell with a fiber period of 2.53 Å.U. and a density of 1.10. The nearest distance between atoms belonging to different chains is 4.3 Å. The shape of the molecules is the simplest plane, zigzag hydrocarbon chain, which complies with the C-C distance of 1.546 Å and the tetrahedrone angle. Figure 104 shows the carbon skeleton of such a chain, without having the hydrogen atoms located. It seems that such an arrangement is very favorable from the point of view of fitting into a crystal lattice. It is found in all medium-length paraffin chains, in polyethylene, and in other vinyl deriva-tives. It seems that substitution (OH, CH_3, Cl) can be car-ried out to a certain extent without interfering with the con-figuration shown in Figure 104. However, as soon as the substituents are voluminous or exhibit strong interaction, the chains may be forced into a more complicated structure. We shall see later during the discussion of certain vinyl de-rivatives how the internal shape of the chain and their ar-rangement in the lattice depend upon the amount and kind of substitution.

Polyethylene has a comparatively high melting point, which is due to the fact that, although the forces are small, the chains are relatively easy to fit into a crystal lattice with-out changing very much the average shape which they have in the melt. Upon melting, the chains start to rotate and oscillate more vigorously, but it seems that in small volumes their individual segments still remain parallel and form an arrangement which may be called mesomorphous and has been also observed with chains of shorter length.

POLYVINYL ALCOHOL

This material is prepared by saponification of polyvinyl acetate, which is in turn obtained by the polymerization of vinyl acetate in the liquid phase around 40°-50° C. with a peroxide catalyst. The polymerization degree of the technical samples is somewhere between 400 and 800, but specimens of much higher molecular weight have also been prepared. The material crystallizes readily upon rolling or stretching, and under certain conditions seems to give comparatively large crystallized areas. The X-ray diagrams are fair and allow a reasonable analysis of the fine structure. The fiber period is 2.52 Å; the theoretical density is 1.31 while the experimental is 1.29 [21] [30] [59].

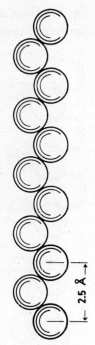

Fig. 104. Structure of the chains of polyethylene.

Identity period and intensity characteristics of the patterns indicate that the fine structure of the chains is such as shown in Figure 105. The backbone of the molecule is a planar zigzag hydrocarbon chain of the type Figure 104. The hydroxyl groups are in the head-to-tail configuration, which agrees with the chemical analysis of polyvinyl acetate as carried out by Marvel and his collaborators [54] [55]. All hydroxyl groups of one chain are in the same plane. The distance between two subsequent hydroxyl groups is 2.52 Å. This indicates, according to Mooney [59], that the chains are stiffened by a thoroughgoing series of hydrogen bonds along their axis. One can also say that polyvinyl alcohol chains are built up by rings containing 3 carbon atoms, 2 oxygen atoms, and 1 hydrogen bridge. Such a 6-membered ring would be quite a favorable geometrical arrangement from the point of view of space requirements, and seems responsible for the ease with which polyvinyl alcohol crystallizes as compared to other vinyl derivatives.

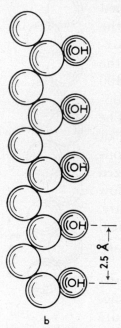

b

Fig. 105. Structure of the chains of polyvinyl alcohol.

The mutual arrangement of the chains in the lattice indicates the existence of other hydrogen bonds, which lead from the oxygen atoms of one chain to the carbon atoms of the next chain. If such a hydrogen bond cross linking between the chains is assumed, one gets a three-dimensional system of forces throughout the crystal, which can explain the tendency of forming comparatively large organized areas of high thermal stability. Of course, such a setup is very sensitive to water, because, as soon as the hydrogen bonds are dissolved, the bonds between the molecules and also the forces which straighten the single chain are very much weakened and the system collapses into a disordered state.

The structure as sketched above seems also to explain the rubbery nature of polyvinyl alcohol in the wet state, because the weakening of the hydrogen bonds converts the whole structure into a hydrocarbon-like system in which crystals must be supported by external forces. Even in highly oriented and extended samples there is always some amorphous background left, which apparently is responsible for the comparatively large elongation to break of this material, and for the comparatively high elastic limit.

POLYVINYL CHLORIDE

Polyvinyl chloride is made by direct polymerization of the monomer in the gaseous or liquid phase. It has been investigated with X ray and electrons but no complete unit-cell determination has been carried out as yet. The fiber period has been recorded with certainty to be 5.0 Å. This either points to a deformation of the simplest zigzag carbon chain in the direction of another planar or a helicoidal arrangement, or has its reason in the fact that the substituents are not all in the same plane. Compare Figure 106.

Looking at the interstices between the chains, one finds that the distance between a given chlorine atom of one chain and the next carbon atom of the neighbor chain is between 2.8 and 2.9 Å. This is what one would expect if a hydrogen bridge would lead from the chlorine atoms of one chain to the carbon atoms of the next chain. This bond is provided by the hydrogen atom of the methylene group, which is in a favorable position to resonate between carbon and chlorine. Extending such hydrogen bonds throughout the lattice, one comes

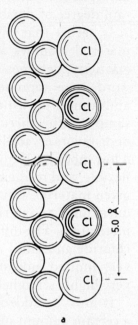

FIG. 106. Structure of the chains of polyvinyl chloride.

to a system of crystal-forming forces which can explain the tendency of polyvinyl chloride to give distinct X-ray patterns under the influence of stretching and which also explains the stability of those crystals when they are once formed.

However, if those forces are weakened by the presence of hydrogen-bond-dissolving agents (plasticizers), one has to expect a tendency to curl up and this may explain the position of polyvinyl chloride on the border line between rubbers and plastics. If one stretches or rolls samples of polyvinyl chloride, one never obtains complete crystallization. There is always an appreciable amount of the substance left in the amorphous or disordered state and that provides for a certain degree of flexibility and resilience.

It seems that always if one favors crystallization, the material assumes a higher modulus but a lower range of elasticity, becomes harder, tougher, and stronger. In other words, one approaches the fiber type. Rolling, stretching, and annealing usually help to change the properties of a sample in this direction. On the other hand, if one prevents or disfavors crystallization, samples are obtained which have a low modulus but a long range of elasticity. They are soft, flexible, and resilient. One approaches the rubber type of the given material. Usually this can be achieved by swelling or quenching, and in the case of synthetic products, by copolymerization. The different types of copolymers between vinyl chloride and vinyl acetate or acrylic derivatives show only very limited indications for crystallization unless they are very highly stretched.

It must be added that there is experimental evidence for a certain amount of branching and cross linking during the polymerization of vinyl chloride and its copolymers. These side reactions affect the structure and mechanical behavior of the material, and make it difficult to draw conclusions without knowing at least qualitatively about the amount of cross linking and branching.

POLYVINYL ACETATE AND POLYSTYRENE

Both these materials have been investigated with X rays repeatedly. They all exhibit an amorphous pattern, which indicates qualitatively the existence of irregularly folded-up

chain molecules. Up to date, all attempts to provoke crystallization of these substances and even to obtain at least
a certain orientation in the amorphous diagrams have failed.
It is not easy to explain just why these polyvinyl derivatives
should be so reluctant to crystallize, but there may be various reasons [12] [82].

First, a certain amount of branching is indicated experimentally in the case of polystyrene, and that is presumably
also true for polyvinyl acetate. Second, there may be a certain irregularity in the structure of the individual chains due
to variations in the head-to-head and head-to-tail arrangement. Finally, it may be that the bulky phenyl and acetyl
residues attached on comparatively flexible chains interfere
with a perfect geometrical order. Similar observations have
been made for acrylic esters, while acrylonitril shows a fair
X-ray diagram if sufficiently stretched.

POLYISOBUTYLENE

This substance is amorphous in the unstretched state at
room temperature, but crystallizes upon stretching. The
melting point of the crystallized phase depends upon stress
and for a highly stretched sample has been found to be
around 50° C.

The amorphous diagram shows a diffuse ring which has
not yet been evaluated by a thorough intensity study. However, an interesting fact can be observed by comparing the
amorphous rings in different polyhydrocarbons. If there is
no methyl group in the system (polyethylene and polybutadiene), the spacing which corresponds to the amorphous ring
is around 4.5 Å, which is close to the average distance of
shorter paraffin chains in the melt. As more and more methyl
groups are introduced in the chain, this average intermolecular distance increases gradually until in polyisobutylene it
reaches a value around 6.2 Å. This indicates that the methyl

groups widen up the disordered phase and do not let the segments of the chains arrange themselves in a close packing.

The crystallized phase has been investigated by Brill and Halle [21] and more recently and thoroughly by Fuller, Frosch, and Pape [22]. The fiber period is 18.63 Å.U. The chains are not in one of the simple planar arrangements, but show a more complex spiral structure which is indicated by the long identity period. It seems that these more highly substituted chains need a larger number of monomers in order to restore geometrical identity. Hence they cannot so easily be fitted into a crystal lattice as can polyethylene or polyvinyl alcohol. We may, therefore, conclude that polyisobutylene, where the forces between the molecules are small and also the chains are incapable of bringing back identical conditions in a short period, will be reluctant to crystallize and therefore will behave as a *rubber*. This is in fact true, and polyisobutylene is one of the most rubber-like polyhydrocarbons which have been investigated up to date [48].

POLYVINYLIDENE CHLORIDE

This substance shows a mesomorphous diagram in the unstretched state, which upon drawing is converted into a crystalline phase giving a comparatively sharp fiber diagram. Fuller [21] and Goggin and Lowry [26] have studied the behavior of polyvinylidene chloride and its X-ray diagrams, and found that the monomers are arranged in the chains according to the head-to-tail structure. The identity period is around 4.7 Å, which indicates that there is a certain deviation from the planar zigzag chain as shown in Figure 107. It seems again that the heavy substitution forces the chain in a coiled shape.

The mechanical behavior of polyvinylidene chloride points to different degrees of randomness in the disordered states, and the process of drawing may be (as with the polyamides) a conversion of internal crystallization of curled-up chains into mutual crystallization between the extended molecules.

The comparatively strong tendency to appear in the crystallized state seems to indicate the action of hydrogen bonds in the lattice and as a consequence polyvinylidene chloride is a plastic with distinct fiber-forming properties.

DIOLEFINE POLYMERS

Diolefine polymers such as polybutadiene, polyisoprene, polydimethyl butadiene and neoprene are of great structural interest because their chains still contain double bonds. This affords for the existence of cis-trans-isomerism, influencing the readiness with which a given substance undergoes crystallization.

Gutta-percha has been found to be trans-polyisoprene, while rubber is the cis-isomer. In both cases the forces between the chains are

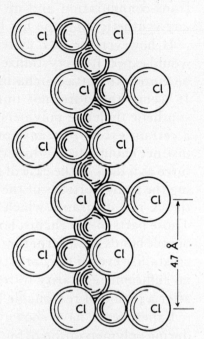

Fig. 107. Structure of the chains of polyvinylidenechloride.

very similar. Nevertheless, gutta crystallizes readily (its melting point is around 60° C.), while rubber (melting point around 6°) shows more tendency for the disordered state. This seems to explain fairly well why cis-polyisoprene is a typical rubber, while the trans-modification behaves at room temperature like a plastic.

The synthetic polydiolefines seem to be mostly copolymers between the cis- and trans-configuration. This is indicated by the fact that polybutadiene, neoprene, and synthetic samples of polyisoprene and polydimethylbutadiene maintain always a considerable amount of uncrystallized material, even if stretched above 800 per cent. The part of the sample which does crystallize upon stretching shows the trans-configuration and up to date no cis-modification of any synthetic diolefine has been observed.

If, however, the *total* material should be trans-isomer, one would expect it to crystallize more easily than it does and to be more like gutta-percha in its behavior than like rubber. It seems, therefore, not unreasonable to assume that the synthetic diolefine polymers are cis-trans-copolymers with a certain excess of trans-configuration. This excess is not distinct enough to produce crystallization without external force as it does in the case of gutta-percha, but upon stretching the trans-portions of the chains crystallize and produce the X-ray diagrams which actually have been observed. Those parts of the chains, however, in which cis- and trans-double bonds are alternating more or less statistically do not crystallize even if they are straightened out, because there is no sufficient regularity to restore identity along the chains after a period of reasonable length.

Experiments have shown that the conditions prevailing during polymerization of butadiene do not affect the character of the X-ray pattern of the crystallized phase, but change the relative amount of the two phases. It may be that the excess of trans-configuration, which usually is prevailing, can account to a certain extent for the fact that rubber shows more tack and adhesion than the different synthetic diolefine polymers, although one has to keep in mind that other effects, such as branching and cross linking, play perhaps a still more important role in the determination of the physical and chemical properties of such materials.

With these general remarks concerning the structure of polymerized diolefines, we shall now pass to their description in detail [50] [56] [58] [79].

POLYBUTADIENE

Samples have been analyzed with X rays which have been prepared by polymerization in the gaseous state with sodium, in the liquid phase with sodium, and alkali-alkyls, and by emulsion polymerization with sodium perborate as catalyst.

The unstretched samples give in all cases amorphous rings, while stretching above 300 per cent produces a crystal diagram of very moderate sharpness and intensity, showing that the larger amount of the material is still in the unorganized and disordered state. The identity period observed is around 5.0 Å, which shows that the chains in the crystallized areas exhibit transconfiguration. Figure 108 shows a sketch of this arrangement. Experiments have been made in searching for an identity period between 8 and 9 Å which would correspond to the cis-configuration, but although the conditions during the polymerization reaction have been widely varied, no indication of this type of lattice has ever been obtained. It seems,

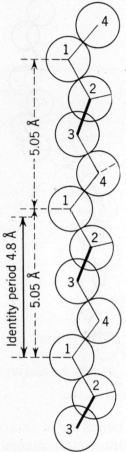

FIG. 108. Structure of the chains of trans-poly-butadiene.

therefore, that the material which does not undergo crystallization even at elongations up to 800 per cent represents

a copolymer of the cis- and trans-configuration, an example
of which is sketched in Figure 109.

POLYISOPRENE

The trans-configuration has two modifications: α- and β-gutta-percha. They
have both been studied very thoroughly by Meyer and Misch [58] and by
Bunn [9].

β-gutta-percha has an identity period
of 4.8 Å. Its structure is shown in Figure
111. The chains are not only in the trans-
configuration concerning t h e double
bonds, but they are also as straight as
possible from the point of view of the single bonds involved in the chain. Hence,
β-gutta should be most ready to crystallize from all polyisoprenes. This is supported by the experiment in as much as
the β-form is obtained by rapidly cooling
down amorphous gutta from 70° C.

The α-modification has an identity
period of 8.7 Å and can be obtained by
slowly cooling the melt down from 70° C.

Fig. 109. Structure of
the chains of cis-trans-
polybutadiene.

Its structure is shown in Figure 110. It
can be seen that all double bonds are in
the trans-configuration, but the single
bonds are in an arrangement which does not provide for the
most straightened-out shape of the chains. This seems to
explain the longer identity period and the fact that the material needs more time to crystallize than the β-modification.

This cis-configuration of polyisoprene is rubber. Only one
modification is known, but it may be that certain hitherto
unexplained spots in the X-ray diagram of rubber belong to
another modification. The identity period of rubber is 8.2 Å.

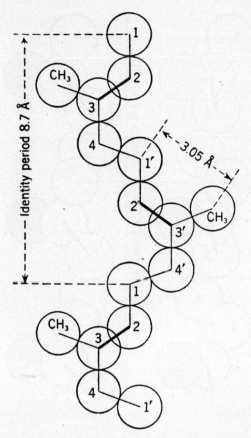

Fig. 110. Structure of the molecular chains of α-gutta percha.

Its structure is shown in Figure 112.   It is probable that the chains are not planar and that the normal valence angles are slightly distorted if the material crystallizes. The bulkiness of the chains and the comparatively small forces between them account for their behavior like rubber [4] [9] [15] [27] [32] [77] [78]. Several attempts have been made to convert rubber into gutta-percha, but it seems that cyclization always takes place with a higher rate than the conversion of the cis- in the trans-configuration.

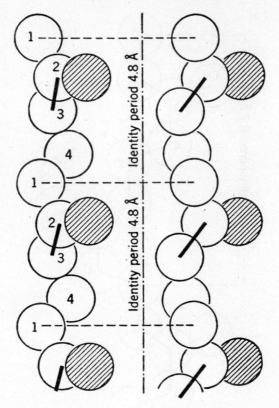

Fig. 111. Structure of the molecular chains of β-gutta percha.

POLYCHLOROPRENE

This material was discovered by Carothers, Collins, Kirby, and Williams [10], and can be obtained by the polymerization of chloroprene in the liquid phase, either without catalyst at room temperature or with catalyst under various experimental conditions. It has been repeatedly investigated with X rays. In the unstretched state, it shows an amorphous pattern which has not yet been analyzed thoroughly. Upon stretching above 300 per cent, it develops a fiber diagram with a fiber period of 4.8 Å. The fiber period shows that the

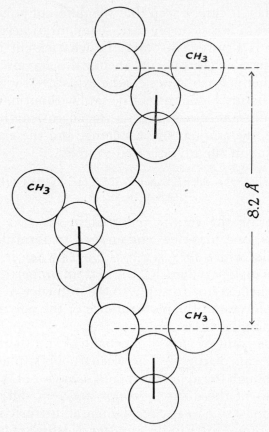

Fig. 112. Structure of the molecular chains of rubber.

trans-configuration prevails in the crystallized part of the material. However, it must be pointed out that just as in the case of polybutadiene, even the best obtainable X-ray diagrams show the presence of a comparatively large amount of disordered material which did escape crystallization. Although nothing positive can be said about the structure of this part, it seems that these portions of the material are copolymers of cis- and trans-configuration having little tendency to crystallize even under considerable elongation.

Altogether, it can be seen that the different polyisoprenes are all more or less favoring trans-configuration except rubber, which is a pure cis-isomer. To what extent the differences in the mechanical and chemical behavior of rubber and the other polyisoprenes can be explained by this difference in structure alone cannot be said without having more detailed information concerning the chain-length distribution curve, the amount of branching, and the existence of cross linking in the investigated samples.

SOME CONCLUSIONS FROM THE FOREGOING PARAGRAPHS

Considering the results reported in the two preceding paragraphs, one may feel encouraged to formulate a few general rules which may serve as guides when it is desired to build up high polymers having certain properties.

One of them seems to apply to the influence of the intermolecular forces on the performance of the polymer under consideration.

From the point of view of mechanical and thermal properties, one can distinguish between rubbers, plastics, and fibers. Although the appearance and behavior of typical representatives of these three groups are very different, this seems not to be due to any fundamental intrinsic structural difference, but is much more a matter of degree of magnitude of the intermolecular forces and the ease with which the chains can be fitted into a crystal lattice.

It has already been mentioned that substances which exhibit small tendency to crystallize represent the rubber type, while materials with high crystallizability display the typical properties of fibers.

The tendency to crystallize is brought about by two factors:

(a) The *forces* between the chains. This influence corresponds to the ΔH-term in the expression for the free energy change during crystallization. If the forces are strong (above 5,000 cals. per mole of the group involved), then they will preponderantly dictate the behavior and we shall expect the material to be a more or less typical fiber. This seems to be true for cellulose, proteins, nylon, and polyvinyl alcohol in the dry state.

(b) The *geometrical bulkiness* of the chains. This influence corresponds to the T Δ S-term in the expression for the free energy change during crystallization. Chains which fit easily into a lattice (polyethylene, trans-polydiolefines) crystallize already under the influence of comparatively weak forces and hence in general have a tendency to appear more fiber-like than one would expect if one considers the forces alone. On the other hand, materials which have very bulky chains do not crystallize even if the intermolecular forces are quite strong. Hence they will be more rubber-like than one would expect on taking into account only the inter-molecular forces (polystyrene, vinyl, copolymers, cellulose, mixed esters, etc.).

Table III is attached to illustrate the possible applica-bility of this consideration. In the first column there is a list of high polymers extending from plyhydrocarbons (having small intermolecular forces) to proteins and polyamides (having strong forces between the chains). The next column shows the type of covalent bond which links the different monomers in each single chain together. Their approximate dissociation energies in cals. per mole of such bond are listed in the next column. It can be seen that they are all above 70,000 cals. per mole, which corresponds to a strong primary valence bond. It has been calculated that the force necessary to rupture such links would correspond approximately to a tensile strength of 150 grams per denier, which is far above any experimentally observed value. The highest tenacities of fibers actually measured so far are around 10 grams per denier. This shows that rupture of the fiber does not pre-

TABLE III

Intermolecular Forces of Some High Polymers and Their Influence on Mechanical Behavior.

Substance	Covalent bond energy along the chains; in cal. per mole.	Molar cohesion pro 5 Å chain length with coördination number four; in cal. per mole.	
Polyethylene	–C–C– 70–80,000	(CH_2)	1,000
Polyisobutylene	–C–C– 70–80,000	(CH_2), (CH_3)	1,200
Polybutadiene	–C=C– 70–120,000	(CH_2), $(CH=CH)$	1,100
Rubber	–C=C– 70–120,000	(CH_2), $(CH=C \cdot CH_3)$	1,300
Polystyrene	–C–C– 70–80,000	(CH_2), (C_6H_5)	4,000
Polychloroprene	–C=C– 70–120,000	(CH_2), $(CH=CCl)$	1,600
Polyvinyl chloride	–C–C– 70–80,000	(CH_2), $(CHCl)$	2,600
Polyvinyl acetate	–C–C– 70–80,000	(CH_2), $(COOCH_3)$	3,200
Polyvinyl alcohol	–C–C– 70–80,000	(CH_2), $(CHOH)$	4,200
Cellulose	–C–O–C– 80–90,000	(OH), $(-O-)$	6,200
Cellulose acetate	–C–O–C– 80–90,000	$(OOCCH_3)$, $(-O-)$	4,800
Polyamides	–C–N–C– 70–90,000	(CH_2), $(CONH)$	5,800
Silk fibroin	–C–N–C– 70–90,000	(CHK), $(CONH)$	9,800

ponderantly involve rupture of the individual chains, but much rather their slipping along each other and the final breaking of Van der Waals' bonds.

The next column contains the groups which are mainly responsible for the mutual attraction of the chains as a consequence of the different types of Van der Waals' forces. In the case of hydrocarbons the attraction is due to unpolar methyl or methylene groups with energies of around 1,000 cals. per mole; in the case of polyamides, one has CONH-groups, which are hydrogen bridged from chain to chain and represent a molar cohesion of around 8,000 cals. per mole.

The forces of all attractive groups accumulate along the chains and provide for a certain molecular cohesion per unit length. The last column of Table III contains the energy values of this cohesion figured out for a length of 5.0 Å under the assumption that each chain is surrounded by four others (specific molecular cohesion). The coördination number of four for parallelized main valence chains is suggested by the

X-ray structure of most of the substances listed in the table.

The figures of the last column show that all typical rubbers (natural rubber, neoprene, polybutadiene, polyisobutylene) have a specific molar cohesion between 1,000 and 2,000 calories. The only exception is polyethylene, where the forces are also small but where the rubber-like properties are not specifically pronounced. As already mentioned, this may be explained by an exceedingly good fitting of the straight zigzag hydrocarbon chains in the crystal lattice.

If the specific molar cohesion as listed in the last column assumes values above 5,000 calories, the substance behaves typically as a fiber with a high modulus of elasticity and a considerable tensile strength. It seems again that the ease with which a given chain can be arranged in a lattice determines the position of the material among the fibers. Thus, nylon is generally stronger and tougher than silk, although its specific molar cohesion is smaller.

In cases when the molar cohesion as listed in column 4 is between 2,000 and 5,000 calories, the material behaves like a plastic; it becomes soft or rubber-like at elevated temperatures but shows crystallization at normal temperatures already without stretching. Polyvinyl alcohol, which has particularly smooth chains, shows again a tendency to exhibit fiber properties, although according to its intermolecular attraction it should be a typical plastic.

It must be understood that Table IV represents only a very crude first attempt to correlate the properties of rubbers, plastics, and fibers from the point of view of intermolecular attraction and to formulate a rule which may serve as a guide for somebody who wants to synthesize a material of given properties.

Other general rules seem to be:

Any increase of the polymerization degree increases tenacity, impact strength, elongation, etc. but decreases the fluidity and filtrability of spinning or casting solutions.

TABLE IV—CONNECTION BETWEEN VARIOUS PROPERTIES OF
HIGH POLYMERS AND THEIR STRUCTURAL CHARACTERISTICS.

Particular property \ Structural feature	Average polymerization degree	Branching	Cross linking	Homopolar nature	Heteropolar groups	Flexibility of chains	Readiness of chains to crystallize	Orientation of crystallites
Modulus of elasticity	+	..	+	..	..	−	+	+
Ultimate tensile strength	+	..	..	−	+	−	+	+
Ultimate impact strength	+	..	−	+	..	+	−	−
Elongation to break	+	..	−	+	..	+	−	−
Range of elastic extensibility	+	−	−	..	..	+	..	..
Surface hardness	+	..	+	−	+	−	+	..
Resistance against temperature	+	..	+	−	+	..	..	..
Electric resistance	..	..	+	+	−	..	..	..
Dielectric constant	..	..	..	−	+	..	..	..
Resistance against swelling	+	+	+	..	..	−	+	+
Resistance against moisture	+	..	+	..	..	−	+	+
Resistance against acids	..	..	+	+	..	..	+	..
Resistance against alkalis	..	..	+	+	..	..	+	..
Adhesive power	..	+	−	..	..	+	−	−

+ means that the structural feature under consideration (*i.e.*, branching) increases the property under consideration (*i.e.*, resistance against swelling). — means that it decreases it. Two points mean that we do not know how the properties are affected by the structural feature.

Moderate branching changes the flow properties of a given polymer in the melt and in solution, but does not seem to affect very drastically the mechanical properties such as tenacity or elongation to break.

Cross linking increases very definitely the heat and swelling resistance of a given material but at the same time reduces the elongation to break, the flexibility, and the impact strength.

The chemical nature of the monomer (or monomers) is mainly responsible for the reaction of the material toward moisture and chemical aggression (oxygen, acids, alkalis). Homopolar constituents (ethylene, butadiene, isoprene, styrene) are comparatively resistant, polar groups or link-ages (hydroxyl, ether, ester, salt) introduce a certain amount of reactivity with moisture or chemicals and eventually make the material valueless for certain purposes. On the other hand, such groups are necessary to fix dyestuffs on the high polymer or to carry out certain chemical changes with them, *i.e.*, mercerization.

The chemical structure of the monomer is at the same time responsible for the intermolecular forces and therefore in great part for the physical behavior of the substance. Hence, the chemical reactivity of a polymer and its mechanical properties are closely interconnected with each other, just as the chemical structure of a low molecular weight compound affects its melting point or solubility.

It seems possible that these general rules may be of some advantage if a polymer of desired properties is to be synthesized; they relieve the chemist from being forced to aim at a close copy of some natural product and permit him to exhibit a certain degree of independent, creative imagination.

In order to give a rough preliminary idea as to how such rules may be formulated, Table IV is attached here. It shows the connection of some properties of high polymers with their structural characteristics. The different lines of this table contain certain properties, such as tenacity, impact strength, electric resistance, etc., while the columns contain the structural features, such as average polymerization degree, branching, cross linking, intermolecular forces, etc.

If a certain structural characteristic, *i.e.*, cross linking, increases a certain property, *i.e.*, temperature resistance, a plus sign is placed at the corresponding place in the table. If it decreases it, a minus sign is introduced. If it does not affect it or if the connection is not known, a point or a question mark appears in the table.

It will be recognized that this way of presentation is very crude and preliminary but it may at least serve to show what kind of help the synthetic chemist may expect from theoretical considerations.

At present, our fundamental knowledge is still incomplete and unsettled but it will increase and improve gradually. As it grows it will put at the disposal of the chemist and engineer rules and relations of increasing reliability and efficiency which he can use to design new polymers. And there can be little doubt that this will finally lead to the discovery and production of synthetic high polymers which will have far better properties than any natural product.

REFERENCES

CHAPTER I

"Galaxies" by Harlow Shapley.

BAKER, R. H. Astronomy. Van Nostrand, New York, 1938.

CURTIS, H. D. The nebulae. *Handbuch der Astrophysik, V*, chap. VI, 1933.

EDDINGTON, A. S. The nature of the physical world. Macmillan, New York, 1928.

HUBBLE, EDWIN. The realm of the nebulae. Yale University Press, New Haven, 1936: also chapter II of this volume.

JEANS, J. H. The mysterious universe. Macmillan, New York, 1932.

SHAPLEY, H. Siderial explorations. Rice Institute Pamphlet, XVIII, No. 2, 1931.

—— Galaxies. Blakiston, Philadelphia, 1942.

CHAPTER II

"The Problem of the Expanding Universe" by Edwin Hubble.

No extensive bibliography is furnished because the list would be largely a repetition of the carefully selected bibliography compiled by H. P. Robertson as an appendix to his discussion of "The Expanding Universe," published in *Science in Progress, Second Series,* 1940. Robertson's contribution to the series is the clearest nontechnical presentation of the fundamental problem of cosmology that has yet appeared.

A few papers, subsequent to Robertson's bibliography, are listed below.

EDDINGTON, SIR ARTHUR. The speed of recession of the extragalactic nebulae. Festschrift für Elis Strömgren, Copenhagen, 1940. Derives the rates of expansion as an *a priori datum,* and finds a numerical value agreeing with the observed value within the uncertainties of the data.

HUBBLE, EDWIN. The motion of the galactic system among the nebulae. *Jour. Frank. Inst., 228,* 131, 1939. Cites evidence suggesting that the law of red shifts does not operate within the Local Group.

SHAPLEY, HARLOW. Various discussions of counts of nebulae, and their bearing on the problem of the general distribution. The papers are found in vols. *23, 24, 25,* and *26* of the *Proc. Nat. Acad. Sci.,* 1938–41; also chapter I of this volume. Emphasis is placed on small-scale irregularities of distribution and the role played by the great cloud of nebulae in Centaurus.

CHAPTER III

"Energy Production in Stars" by Hans A. Bethe.

Books and Review Articles.

BETHE, H. A., and MARSHAK, R. E. Progress report. Physical Society of London, vol. VI, 1940.

CHANDRASEKHAR, S. Introduction to theory of stellar structure. 1939.

EDDINGTON, A. S. Internal constitution of stars. 1926.

Original Articles on Theory of Energy Production.

ATKINSON, R. D'E., and HOUTERMANS, F. G. Z. *Phys., 54,* 656, 1929

BETHE, H. A. *Phys. Rev., 55,* 434, 1939.

—— *Astrophys. Jour., 92,* 118, 1940.

—— and CRITCHFIELD, C. L. *Phys. Rev. 54,* 248, 1938.

GAMOW, G. *Phys. Rev., 55,* 718, 1939.

—— and TELLER, E. *Phys. Rev., 53,* 608, 1938.

—— *Phys. Rev., 55,* 791, 1939.

MARSHAK, R. E. *Astrophys. Jour., 92,* 321, 1940.

—— *Annals, New York Acad. of Sci.,* March, 1941.

WEIZSACKER, C. F. VON. *Phys. Z., 39,* 633, 1939.

WILDHACK, W. A. *Phys. Rev., 57,* 81, 1940.

Further Articles on Internal Constitution of Stars.

BLANCH, LOWAN, MARSHAK, and BETHE. *Astrophys. Jour., 94,* 37, 1941.

COWLING, T. G. *M. N. Roy. Astr. Soc., 96,* 42, 1938.

EDDINGTON, A. S. *M. N. Roy. Astr. Soc., 99,* 595, 1939.

MORSE, P. M. *Astrophys. Jour., 92,* 27, 1940.

OPPENHEIMER, J. R., and VOLKOFF, G. M. *Phys. Rev., 55,* 374, 1939.

STROMGREN, B. *Astrophys. Jour., 87,* 520, 1938.

CHAPTER IV

"Image Formation by Electrons" by V. K. Zworykin.

Busch, H. Calculation of the paths of cathode rays in axially symmetric electromagnetic fields. *Annalen der Physik, 81,* 974–993, 1926.

Knoll, M., and Ruska, E. Geometric electron optics. *Annalen der Physik, 12,* 607–661, 1932.

Zworykin, V. K. Electron optics. *Jour. Frank. Inst. 215,* 535–555, 1933.

Gans, R. Electron paths in electron-optical systems. *Zeitschr. f. tech. Physics, 18,* 41–48, 1937.

Ramberg, E. G., and Morton, G. A. Electron optics. *Jour. App. Phys., 10,* 465–478, 1939.

Zworykin, V. K. The iconoscope—a modern version of the electric eye. *Proc. Inst. Radio Engineers, 22,* 16–32, 1934.

Zworykin, V. K., and Morton, G. A. Applied electron optics. *Jour. of the Optical Soc. of Am., 26,* 181–189, 1936.

Zworykin, V. K. Television with cathode-ray tube for receiver. *Radio Eng., 9,* Nr. 12, 38–41, 1929.

Iams, H., Morton, G. A., and Zworykin, V. K. The image iconoscope. *Proc. Inst. Radio Engineers, 27,* 541–547, 1939.

Borries, B. v., and Ruska, E. Properties of supermicroscopic imaging. *Naturwiss., 27,* 279–287, 1939.

Zworykin, V. K., Hillier, J., and Vance, A. W. An electron microscope for practical laboratory service. *Electrical Eng., 60,* 157–161, 1941.

Hillier, J., and Vance, A. W. Recent developments in the electron microscope. *Proc. Inst. Radio Engineers, 29,* 167–176, 1941.

Morton, G. A. A survey of research accomplishments with the RCA electron microscope. *RCA Rev., 6,* 131–166, 1941.

CHAPTER V

"Some Recent Work in the Field of High Pressures" by P. W. Bridgman.

A general survey of the high-pressure field up to the time of its publication will be found in my book, *The Physics of High Prssures.* Macmillan, 1931.

1. Amagat, E. H. *Ann. Chim. Phys., 29,* 68, 1893.
2. Tammann, G. Kristallisieren und Schmelzen. Barth, Leipzig, 1903.
3. Bridgman, P. W. *Phil. Mag.,* July, 1912, p. 63; *Jour. App. Phys., 9,* 517, 1938; *Mech. Eng.,* Feb., 1939.
4. —— *Jour. Am. Chem. Soc., 36,* 1344, 1914; *38,* 609, 1916.
5. Jacobs, R. B. *Jour. Chem. Phys., 5,* 945, 1937.
6. Starr, Chauncey. *Phys. Rev., 54,* 210, 1938.
7. Bridgman, P. W. *Proc. Am. Acad., 59,* 165, 1923.
8. Born, Max. Atomtheorie des festen Zustandes. Teubner, Leipzig, 1923.
9. Ewell, R. H., and Eyring, H. *Jour. Chem. Phys., 726,* 1937.
10. Bridgman, P. W. *Proc. Am. Acad., 68,* 27, 1933.
11. —— *Phys. Rev., 48,* 825, 1935.
12. Rossini, F. D., and Jessup, R. S. *Nat. Bur. Stds.,* Research Paper RP1141, 1938.
13. Bridgman, P. W. *Proc. Am. Acad., 72,* 45, 1937; *72,* 227, 1938.
14. —— *Jour. Chem. Phys., 9,* 794, 1941.
15. —— *Proc. Am. Acad., 74,* 1, 1940.
16. —— *Proc. Am. Acad., 74,* 11, 1940.
17. —— *Phys. Rev., 57,* 342, 1940.
18. Griggs, D. T. *Jour. Geol., 44,* 541, 1936.
19. Basset, J. *Jour. de Phys. et le Rad., 1,* 121, 1940.
20. Bridgman, P. W. *Phys. Rev., 60,* 351, 1941.
21. —— *Jour. App. Phys., 12,* 461, 1941.

CHAPTER VI

"Recent Developments in Power Generation"
by Lionel S. Marks.

1. Jeffries, Harold. The earth, 2d ed., p. 277. Cambridge Univ. Press, 1929.
2. The Smith-Putnam wind turbine. Various authors. *Mech. Eng., 63,* 473, 1941.
3. Galbraith, C. C. The Kaplan turbine. *Eng. News-Record, 118,* 765, 1937.
4. Baur and Phillips. *Gerlands Beiträge zur Geophysik, 42,* 232, 1934; also *45,* 1935, and *47,* 1936.
5. Transeau, E. N. *Ohio Jour. of Sci., 26,* 1, 1926.
6. Marks, L. S. Mech. engineers' handbook. 4th ed., p. 432. McGraw-Hill, 1941.

7. *Electrical World,* October 18, 1941.
8. HACKETT, H. N. Mercury for the generation of light, heat and power. SMITH, A. R., and THOMPSON, E. S. The mercury-vapor process. *Trans. A. S. M. E.,* December, 1941.
9. MARKS, L. S. Mech. engineers' handbook. 4th ed., p. 426.
10. MARKS, L. S., and DANILOV, M. The gas turbine. *Trans. A. S. M. E., 46,* 1095, 1924.
11. KELLER, C., and MARKS, L. S. Axial-flow fans. McGraw-Hill, 1937.
12. MEYER, A. The combustion gas turbine. *Mech. Eng., 61,* 645, 1939.

CHAPTER VII

"Some Fundamental Aspects of Photosynthesis" by James Franck.

1. EINSTEIN, A. *Ann. Physik, 37,* 832, 1912.
2. SPOEHR, H. A. Photosynthesis. Chem. Catal. Co., 1926.
3. McALISTER, E. D. *Smithsonian Miscell. Coll., 95,* 24, 1937.
4. FRANCK, J., and GAFFRON, H. Photosynthesis, facts and interpretations. In: Advances in enzymology, Interscience Publishers, 1941.
5. —— and LIVINGSTON, R. *Jour. Chem. Physics, 9,* 184, 1941.
6. —— and HERZFELD, K. F. *Jour. Phys. Chem., 41,* 97, 1937.
7. ZSCHEILE, F. B., and GOMAR, C. L. *Bot. Gaz., 102,* 463, 1941.
8. WARBURG, O., and NEGELEIN, E. *Zeitschr. Phys. Chem. 106,* 191, 1923.
9. MANNING, W. M., STAUFFER, J. F., DUGGAR, B. M., and DANIELS, F. *Jour. Am. Chem. Soc., 60,* 266, 1938.
10. EMERSON, R., and LEWIS, C. M. *Am. Jour. Bot., 26,* 808, 1939.
11. RIEKE, F. F. (Unpublished.)
12. HOOVER, W. H., JOHNSTON, E. S., and BRACKETT, F. S. *Smithsonian Miscell. Coll., 87,* No. 16, p. 1.
13. EMERSON, R., and ARNOLD, W. *Jour. Gen. Physiol., 15,* 391, 1932.
14. FRANCK, J., and HERZFELD, K. F. *Jour. Phys. Chem., 45,* 978, 1941.
15. McALISTER, E. D., and MYERS, J. E. *Smithsonian Miscell. Coll., 99,* No. 6, 1940.
16. FRANCK, J., FRENCH, C. S., and PUCK, T. T. *Jour. Phys. Chem., 45,* 1268, 1941.
17. WASSINK, E. C., KATZ, E., and coworkers. *Enzymologia, 4,* 254, 1937; *5,* 100, 1938; and *6,* 145, 1939.

18. Weller, S., and Franck, J. *Jour. Phys. Chem.*, *45*, 1359, 1941.
19. Ruben, S., Kamen, M. D., and coworkers. *Jour. Am. Chem. Soc.*, *61*, 661, 1939; *62*, 3451, 1940; *62*, 3443, 1940; *62*, 3450, 1940. *Proc. Nat. Acad. Sci.* (U. S.), *26*, 418, 1940. *Science, 90*, 570, 1939.
20. Kautsky, H., and coworkers. *Naturwissenschaften, 19*, 964, 1931; *19*, 1043, 1931; *24*, 317, 1936; *26*, 576, 1938; *Ber., 65*, 1762, 1932; *66*, 1588, 1933; *68*, 152, 1935; *Biochem. Z., 274*, 423, 1934; *274*, 435, 1934; *277*, 250, 1935; *278*, 373, 1935; *302*, 1137, 1939.
21. Blinks, L. R., and Skow, R. K. *Proc. Nat. Acad. Sci., 24*, 420, 1938.
22. Garner, W. W., and Allard, H. A. *Jour. Agr. Res., 42*, 645, 1931.

CHAPTER VIII

"The Structure of Liquids" by John G. Kirkwood.

Bernal. Structure and molecular forces in liquids. *Trans. Faraday Soc., 33*, 27, 1937.
—— and Fowler. *Jour. Chem. Phys., 1*, 515, 1933.
Debye and Mencke. *Phys. Zeit., 31*, 797, 1930.
Eisenstein and Gingrich. *Phys. Rev., 58*, 307, 1940.
Eyring and Hirschfelder. *Jour. Phys. Chem., 41*, 249, 1937.
Fowler, R. H. Statistical mechanics. 2d ed., Cambridge Press, 1936.
Kirkwood. *Jour. Chem. Phys., 3*, 300, 1935.
—— and Monroe. *Jour. Chem. Phys., 9*, 514, 1941.
—— *Jour. Chem. Phys.*, in press, 1942.
Lark-Horowitz and Miller. *Nature, 146*, 459, 1940.
Lennard-Jones and Corner. *Proc. Roy. Soc.* (London), *A178*, 401, 1941.
—— and Devonshire, *Proc. Roy. Soc.* (London), *A163*, 53, 1937; *A170*, 464, 1939.
Meyer. *Jour. Chem. Phys., 5*, 67, 1937.
—— and Montroll. *Jour. Chem. Phys., 9*, 2, 1941.
Prins. *Zeit. f. Physik, 56*, 617, 1929.
Rushbrooke and Coulson. *Phys. Rev., 56*, 1216, 1939.
Stewart. *Rev. Mod. Phys., 2*, 116, 1930.
Wall. *Phys. Rev., 58*, 307, 1940.
Warren. *Jour. Appl. Phys., 8*, 645, 1937.
—— *Phys. Rev., 44*, 969, 1933.
Zernicke and Prins. *Zeit. f. Physik, 41*, 184, 1927.

CHAPTER IX

"The Mode of Action of Sulfanilamide" by Perrin H. Long.

ANSBACHER, S. *Science, 93*, 164, 1941.
BARRON, E. S. G., and JACOBS, H. R. *Proc. Soc. Exper. Biol. Med., 37*, 10, 1937.
BLISS, E. A., and LONG, P. H. *Bull. Johns Hopkins Hosp., 60*, 149, 1937.
—— *Bull. Johns Hopkins Hosp.,* —, 1940.
BOSSE, O. A. Inaug. dissert. dok. med., Marburg, 1935.
BUTTLE, G. A. H. *Proc. Roy. Soc. Med., 31*, 154, 1937.
CARPENTER, C. M. *Abstr. Third Internat. Congress Microbiol.,* p. 256, 1939.
—— and BARBOUR, G. M. *Proc. Soc. Exper. Biol. Med., 41*, 354, 1939.
—— HAWLEY, P. L., and BARBOUR, G. M. *Science, 88*, 530, 1938.
—— *Jour. Bact., 36*, 280, 1938.
—— *Jour. Pediat., 14*, 116, 1939.
CHU, H. I., and HASTINGS, A. B. *Jour. Pharmacol. and Exper. Therap., 63*, 407, 1938.
COLEBROOK, L., and KENNY, M. *Lancet, 1*, 1279, 1936.
—— BUTTLE, G. A. H., and O'MEARA, R. A. Q. *Lancet, 2*, 1323, 1936.
DOMAGK, G. *Deutsche med. Wochenschr, 61*, 250, 1935.
—— *Klin. Wochenschr., 15*, 1585, 1936.
—— *Dermat. Wochenschr., 107*, 797, 1938.
—— *Zeitschr. f. klin. Med., 132*, 775, 1937.
—— *L'Europe méd.,* Vol. IV, Nos. 3 and 4, 1939.
DORFMAN, A., RICE, L,. KOSER, S. A., and SAUNDERS, F. *Proc. Soc. Exper. Biol. Med., 45*, 750, 1940.
FILDES, P. *Lancet, 1*, 955, 1940.
FLEMING, A. *Jour. Path. and Bact., 50*, 69, 1940.
FOURNEAU, E., TREFOUEL, J., TREFOUEL, MME. J., NITTI, F., and BOVET, D. *Compt. rend. de soc. de biol., 122*, 652, 1936.
FOX, C., CLINE, J. E., OTTENBERG, R. *Jour. Pharmacol. Exper. Therap., 66*, 99, 1939.
FOX, C., GERMAN, B., and JANEWAY, C. A. *Proc. Soc. Exper. Biol. Med., 40*, 184, 1939.
FULLER, A. T. *Lancet, 1*, 194, 1937.
—— and MAXTED, W. R. *Brit. Jour. Exper. Path., 20*, 177, 1939.
GARROD, L. P. *Lancet, 1*, 1125, 1178, 1938.
GREEN, H. N. *Brit. Jour. Exp. Path., 21*, 38, 1940.

KEMP, H. A. *Texas State Jour. Med., 34,* 208, 1938.

KING, J. T., HENSCHEL, A. F., and GREEN, B. S. *Proc. Soc. Exper. Biol. Med., 38,* 810, 1938.

LEVADITI, C. *Monogr. de l'inst. A. Fournier,* No. 5, 1937.

LEVADITI, C, and VAISMAN, A. *Compt. rend. de acad. de sci., 200,* 1694, 1935.

—— *Compt. rend. de soc. de biol., 119,* 946, 1935.

—— *Presse méd., 43,* 2097, 1935.

LEVADITI, C., and VAISMAN, A. *Compt. rend. de soc. de biol., 120,* 1077, 1935.

—— *Compt. rend. de acad. de sci., 205,* 1108, 1937.

LOCKE, A., MAIN, E. R., and MELLON, R. R. *Jour. Immunol., 36,* 183, 1938.

—— *Science, 88,* 620, 1938.

LOCKE, A., and MELLON, R. R. *Science, 90,* 231, 1939.

LOCKWOOD, J. S. *Jour. Immunol., 35,* 155, 1938.

—— and LYNCH, H. M. *Jour. Am. Med. Assn., 114,* 935, 1940.

LONG, P. H., and BLISS, E. A. *Jour. Am. Med. Assn., 108,* 32, 1937.

—— The clinical and experimental use of sulfanilamide, sulfapyridine, and allied compounds. The Macmillan Company, New York, 1939.

—— *Can. Med. Assn. Jour., 37,* 457, 1937.

—— *South. Med. Jour., 30,* 479, 1937

—— and FEINSTONE, W. H. *Jour. Am. Med. Assn., 112,* 115, 1939.

MCLEOD, C. M. *Proc. Soc. Exper. Biol. and Med., 41,* 69, 1939.

—— *Jour. Exper. Med., 72,* 217, 1940.

MADISON, R. R., and SNOW, J. E. *Proc. Soc. Exper. Biol. Med., 36,* 592, 1937.

MAIN, E. R., SHINN, L. E., and MELLON, R. R. *Proc. Soc. Exper. Biol. Med., 39,* 272, 1938.

MAYER, R. L., and OECHSLIN, C. *Compt. rend. de soc. de biol., 130,* 211, 1939.

—— *Biol. Med., Suppl., 27,* 45, 1937.

MELLON, R. R., LOCKE, A., and SHINN, L. E. *Abstr. Third Internat. Congress Microbiol.,* p. 255, 1939.

—— and BAMBAS, L. L. *Proc. Soc. Exper. Biol. Med., 36,* 682, 1937.

OTTENBERG, R., and FOX, C. *Proc. Soc. Exper. Biol. Med., 38,* 479, 1938.

RUBBO, S. D., and GILLESPIE, J. M. *Nature, 146,* 838, 1940.

SADUSK, J. F., and MANAHAN, C. P. *Jour. Am. Med. Assn., 113,* 14, 1939.

SELBIE, F. R. *Brit. Jour. Exper. Path.*, *21*, 90, 1940.

SHAFFER, P. A. *Science, 89*, 574, 1939.

SHINN, L. E., MAIN, E. R., and MELLON, R. R. *Proc. Soc. Exper. Biol. Med.*, *39*, 591, 1938; *ibid.*, *40*, 640, 1939.

STAMP, T. C. *Lancet, 2*, 10, 1939.

WARREN, J., STREET, J. A., and STOKINGER, H. E. *Proc. Soc. Exper. Biol. Med.*, *40*, 208, 1939.

WEST, R., and COBURN, A. C. *Jour. Exper. Med.*, *72*, 91, 1940.

WHITBY, L. E. H. *Lancet, 2*, 1095, 1938.

WOOD, W. B., JR., and LONG, P. H. *Ann. Int. Med.*, *13*, 612, 1939.

WOODS, D. D. *Brit. Jour. Exper. Path.*, *21*, 74, 1940.

CHAPTER X

"Some Scientific Aspects of the Synthetic Rubber Problem" by H. Mark.

1. ALFREY, T., and MARK, H. Phase transition and mechanical properties of rubber. *Rubber Chem. and Techn.*, *14*, 525, 1941.

2. ASTBURY, W. T. Structure of keratin and myosin. *Nature, 147*, 696, 1941. Fundamentals of fiber structure. Oxford University Press, London, 1933.

3. BAKER, W. O., FULLER, C. S., and PAPE, N. R. Crystallinity of cellulose esters *Jour. Am. Chem. Soc.*, *64*, 776, 1942. Crystallinity of polyamides. *Jour. Am. Chem. Soc.*, *62*, 3275, 1940.

4. BEKKEDAHL, W. Crystallization of rubber. *Proc. Rubber Tech. Conf.*, p. 223. London, 1938.

5. BERNAL, J. D., and FANKUCHEN, I. Molecular structure of proteins. *Nature, 139*, 923, 1937; *172*, 1075, 1938.

6. BLEASE, R. A., and TUCKETT, R. F. Fractionation of vinyl acetate polymers. *Trans. Faraday Soc.*, *37*, 571, 1941.

7. BOJER, R. Unpublished investigations on chain-length, distribution, and branching. Some of the results were presented at the A. A. A. S., Research Conference on High Polymers at Gibson Island, July, 1942.

8. BUNN, C. W. Structure of polyethylene. *Trans. Faraday Soc.*, *35*, 482, 1939.

9. —— Structure and mechanical behavior of polyhydrocarbons. *Proc. Roy. Acad.* (London), *A180*, 40, 67, 82, 1942.

10. CAROTHERS, W. H., and numerous collaborators published about fifty papers on high polymers as the result of their work in the research laboratories of E. I. du Pont Co., Delaware. Reference may be made to the book by W. H. Carothers, Collected papers, Vol. I of the series on High Polymers, Interscience Publishers, New York, 1940.
11. CLARK, G. L. Crystallization and mechanical properties of rubber. *Ind. and Eng. Chem.*, *31*, 1379, 1939; *32*, 1474, 1940.
12. DAVIS, A. L. Thesis at the Polytechnic Institute of Brooklyn, 1941–1943.
13. EYRING, H., and EWELL, R. H. Statistical treatment of long-chain molecules. *Jour. Chem. Phys.*, *4*, 283, 1936; *5*, 726, 1937.
14. FANKUCHEN, I. X-ray studies of proteins. *Cold Spring Harbor Symposium*, *9*, 198, 1941.
15. FIELD, J. E. Crystallized and amorphous areas in rubber. *Jour. Appl. Phys.*, *12*, 23, 1941.
16. FIKENTSCHER, H., and MARK, H. Theory of the elasticity of rubber. *Kautschuk*, *1*, 2, 1930.
17. FLORY, P. J. Molecular weight and viscosity of high polymers. *Jour. Am. Chem. Soc.*, *62*, 1057, 3032, 1940.
18. —— Statistical treatment and distribution curves of polycondensation products. *Jour. Am. Chem. Soc.*, *61*, 3334, 1939; *62*, 2255, 1940; *63*, 3083, 3091, 3096, 1941.
19. FREUDENBERG, K. Tannin, cellulose, tiguin. Berlin, 1933.
20. FROLICH, P. K., *et al.* Preparation of polyisobutylene. *Jour. Am. Chem. Soc.*, *62*, 276, 1940.
21. FULLER, C. S. Comprehensive paper on linear polymers containing many original contributions. *Chem. Rev.*, *26*, 143, 1940.
22. —— FROSCH, C. J., and PAPE, N. R. Structure of polyisobutylene. *Jour. Am. Chem. Soc.*, *62*, 1909, 1940.
23. —— BAKER, W. O., and PAPE, N. R. Crystalline behavior of linear polyamides. *Jour. Am. Chem. Soc.*, *62*, 3275, 1940.
24. —— FROSCH, C. J., and PAPE, N. R. Chain structure of linear polyesters. *Jour. Am. Chem. Soc.*, *64*, 154, 1942.
25. FUOSS, R. M., and MEAD, D. J. Viscosity and molecular weight of polyvinyl chloride. *Jour. Am. Chem. Soc.*, *64*, 277, 1942.
26. FUOSS, R. M. Paper in press. A new osmotic cell for the investigation of high polymers.
27. GEHMAN, S. D., and FIELD, J. E. Crystallization and mechanical properties of rubber. *Jour. Appl. Phys.*, *10*, 564, 1939.

28. Goggin, W. C., and Lowry, R. D. Structure of polyvinylidene chloride. *Ind. and Eng. Chem.*, 34, 327, 1942.

29. Guth, E., and Mark, H. Statistical treatment of long-chain molecules. *Monatsch. Chem.*, 65, 93, 1934; *Naturwiss.*, 25, 353, 1937.

30. Halle, F., and Hofmann, U. Structure of polyvinyl alcohol. *Naturwiss.*, 45, 770, 1935.

31. Harris, M., *et al.* Structure and properties of cotton and wool fibers. *Jour. Res. Nat. Bureau Stand.*, 24, 743; 25, 47, 1940; 26, 93, 205; 27, 89, 181, 1941.

32. Hauser, E. A., and Mark, H. Investigation on the molecular structure of rubber. *Koll. Chem. Beih.*, 22, 64, 1926.

33. Haworth, W. N. The constitution of sugars. E. Arnold, London, 1929.

34. Hermans, P. H. Amorphous constituents of high polymers. *Jour. Phys. Chem.*, 45, 827, 1941.

35. Herzog, R. O., and Jancke, W. *Ang. Chem.*, 34, 385, 1921.

36. Hibbert, H., and collaborators. Papers on the structure and properties of high polymers, particularly cellulose and lignin. *Jour. Am. Chem. Soc.*, 61, 1905, 1910, 1912 (1939); 62, 230, 2140, 2144.

37. Hill, J. W., co-author of many papers with W. H. Carothers. See Carothers, W. H., Collected papers, Interscience Publishers, New York, 1940.

38. Huggins, M. L. Statistical treatment of long-chain molecules. *Jour. Phys. Chem.*, 42, 911; 43, 439, 1938; *Jour. Appl. Phys.*, 10, 700, 1939.

39. Karrer, P. Polymerse Kohlenhydrate. AVG, Leipzig, 1925.

40. Katz, I. R. X-ray diagrams of unstretched and stretched rubber. *Naturwiss.*, 13, 411, 1925.

41. Kemp, A. R., and Peters, H. Viscosity, diffusion, and molecular weight of rubber. *Jour. Phys. Chem.*, 43, 923, 1939.

42. —— Fractionation viscosity and molecular weight of rubber and gutta-percha. *Ind. and Eng. Chem.*, 33, 1263, 1391, 1941. Two more articles are in press.

43. Kraemer, E. O. Use of ultracentrifuge and of viscosity measurements for molecular weight determinations. *Ind. and Eng. Chem.*, 30, 1200, 1938.

44. —— Discussion of the heterogeneity of high polymers. *Jour. Frank. Inst.*, 231, 1, 1941.

45. Kuhn, W. Statistical treatment of long-chain molecules. *Koll. Zs.*, 68, 2, 1934; 76, 258, 1936; 87, 3, 1939.

46. LANGMUIR, I., and WRINCH, D. Molecular structure of folded-up protein chains. *Proc. Phys. Soc., 51,* 1613, 1939.

47. LAUFFER, M. A. Comprehensive article on experimental viscosity work. *Chem. Rev.,* in press.

48. LONDON, F. Van der Waals' forces between long-chain molecules. *Jour. Phys. Chem., 46,* 305, 1942.

49. MACK, E., JR. Curling up of long-chain molecules. *Jour. Phys. Chem., 41,* 221, 1937.

50. MARK, H. Physical chemistry of high polymers, Vol. II of the series on High Polymers, Interscience Publishers, New York, 1940.

51. —— Distribution curve and mechanical behavior of high polymers. *Paper Trade Jour., 113,* 34, 1941.

52. ——Phase transition and elastic behavior of high polymers. *Ind. and Eng. Chem., 34,* 449, 1942.

53. —— and SIMHA, R. Distribution curves of degraded cellulose acetate samples. *Trans. Faraday Soc., 36,* 611, 1940.

54. MARVEL, C. S., *et al.* Molecular structure of chain polymers. *Jour. Am. Chem. Soc., 61,* 3156, 3241, 3244 (1939); *62,* 45, 2666, 3495, 3499 (1940).

55. —— and FRANK, R. L. Kinetic studies on copolymerization. *Jour. Am. Chem. Soc., 64,* 92, 1675 (1942).

56. MEYER, K. H., SUSICH, G., and VALKO, E. Kinetic elasticity of rubber. *Koll. Zs., 59,* 208, 1932.

57. —— and MARK, H. Der Aufbau der hochpolymeren organirchen Naturstoffe. AVG, Leipzig, 1930.

58. —— Natural and synthetic high polymers, Vol. II of the series on High Polymers, Interscience Publishers, New York, 1942.'

59. MOONEY, R. C. L. Structure of polyvinyl alcohol. *Jour. Am. Chem. Soc., 63,* 2828, 1941.

60. NICKERSON, R. F. Crystallized and disordered areas in cellulose. *Ind. and Eng. Chem., 32,* 1022, 1941.

61. OHL, F. Fractionation, viscosity, and tenacity of cellulose acetate. *Kunstseide, 12,* 468, 1930.

62. OTT, E. Structure and mechanical properties of high polymers. *Ind. and Eng. Chem., 32,* 1641, 1940.

63. PAULING, L., and NIEMANN, J. Structure of proteins. *Jour. Am. Chem. Soc., 61,* 1860 (1939).

64. POLANY, M. First attempt to determine the structure of a high polymer with X-rays. *Naturwiss., 9,* 288, 1921.

65. Purves, C. B. Fractions of cellulose with different reactivity. *Jour. Am. Chem. Soc., 64* (1942).

66. Rocha, H. J. Fractionation of cellulose acetate. *Koll. Beih., 30,* 230, 1930.

67. Scherrer, P. In: R. Zsigmondy's Kolloidchemic. 2 Aufl., Leipzig, 1920.

68. Schieber, W. Distribution curve and mechanical properties of cellulose. *Angew. Chem., 52,* 487, 561, 1939.

69. Schulz, G. V., Huseman, E., and Dinglinger, K. Distribution curves and kinetics of polymerization reactions. *Z. S. phys. Chem., B32,* 27, 1936; *B41,* 466; *B43,* 45, 1939; *B46,* 105; *B47,* 155, 1940.

70. Simha, R. Viscosity, molecular size, and molecular shape of high polymers. *Jour. Appl. Phys., 13,* 147, 1942.

71. Spurlin, H. M. Fractionation and flexing strength of nitrocellulose. *Ind. and Eng. Chem., 30,* 538, 1938.

72. Staudinger, H. Der Aufbau der hochmolecularen organischen Substanzen. Berlin, 1932. Also numerous articles in scientific magazines.

73. Straus, F. L., and Levy, R. M. New and very efficient method for the fractionation of cellulose. *Paper Trade Jour., 114,* April 30, 1942.

74. Svedberg, Th., and Pedersen, K. The ultracentrifuge. Oxford, 1940.

75. Taylor, H. S. Several lectures and discussion remarks during the last year, particularly discussions at the ACS meeting in Memphis, Tenn., in April, 1942.

76. Thomas, R. M., Sparks, W. J., Frolich, P. K., Otto, M., and Muller-Cunradi, M. Polymerization of isobutylene. *Jour. Am. Chem. Soc., 62,* 276, 1940.

77. Treloar, L. G. Crystallization of rubber. *Trans. Faraday Soc., 37,* 84, 1941.

78. Warren, E. B., and Simard, G. L. X-ray investigation of unstretched rubber. *Jour. Am. Chem. Soc., 58,* 507, 1936.

79. Woehlisch, E. Kinetic elasticity of muscles and rubber. *Biol. Zs., 85,* 406, 1927; *Koll. Zs., 89,* 239, 1939.

80. Wood, L. A., Bekkedahl, N., and Peters, K. Crystallization of rubber. *Jour. Rest. Nat. Bureau Stand., 23,* 571, 1939.

81. Whitby, G. S., and collaborators. *Trans. Faraday Soc., 32,* 315, 1936; *34,* 128, 1938; *Can. Jour. Res., 4,* 344, 1931; *6,* 203, 280, 1932.

82. WHYTE, D. Unpublished experiments in progress at the Brooklyn Polytechnic Institute.
83. WRINCH, D. Native protein theory. *Cold Spring Harbor Symposium, 9, 218, 1941.*

INDEX